# NOTHING LIKE SCIENCE

Magnus Pyke

# NOTHING LIKE
# SCIENCE

*Illustrated by*
MICHAEL FFOLKES

JOHN MURRAY
FIFTY ALBEMARLE STREET LONDON

*First published 1957*

*Made and printed in Great Britain by*
*Butler & Tanner Ltd, Frome and London*
*and published by John Murray (Publishers) Ltd*

# CONTENTS

# SCIENCE TO LIVE BY

THROUGHOUT history the priesthood, either by accident or intent, has managed to conceal in mystery the philosophy by which people live. In China, only the clergy were able to read the special characters in which the sacred books were written. The Delphic oracle traditionally spoke in ambiguous terms. And in later times, wars have been fought for the right to translate the Bible into plain speech. Today many ordinary people think of scientists as the members of a new priesthood, and otherwise well-educated men and women are as little able to understand what science is about as were the simple peasants of medieval times when confronted by a Greek Testament.

Science has crept up on the Western world as a philosophy of life in a curiously insidious manner. Joseph Priestley looked upon himself primarily as a great divine. In his day his inflammatory Low Church preaching attracted so much opprobrious attention in Birmingham that his windows were smashed by angry crowds and he was eventually forced to emigrate to America. Yet nowadays no normal person would dream of studying his theological opinions. On the other hand, his scientific discoveries led to radical changes in our intellectual comprehension of the nature of fire. Priestley himself looked upon his own scientific experiments as an elegant accomplishment to amuse the visitors and friends of his patron, Lord Shelburne. And it is perhaps true to say the residual traces of this attitude to science exist today, not only among classically educated people but also among some of those who consider themselves to be scientists. We all know that conjuring tricks are done with mirrors or wires or elastic bands, that is to say that they all have a matter-of-fact explanation. In just the same way scientific experiments can all be explained. When the blue litmus paper turns red, it can safely be attributed to acid. When there is a disagreeable smell of bad eggs, hydrogen sulphide is in the air. But science is more than this. Because individual chemical reactions are dramatic and particular experiments possess a certain artistic flamboyance one can easily understand why it is that science is taught as if it *were* merely a conglomeration of infinitely complicated conjuring tricks. Great numbers of boys and girls painfully struggle to learn about calcium and phosphorus and Archimedes and Joule's Law and Centigrade and Fahrenheit. This is why later on adults in their turn, now middle-aged business men and earnest ladies from the better-class suburbs of our great cities, struggle to grasp the facts about automatic telephones, or high-octane motor fuel, or the fattening effect of calories in boiled potatoes.

Modern, twentieth-century people, whether they are children at school or newspaper-readers in later life, learn a whole rag-bag of scientific facts without ever grasping what science itself is about. Similarly the range of Joseph Priestley's interests was far too limited for him to feel the greatness of his philosophical achievement in grasping the fire from heaven, that divine stuff stolen from the gods that had enchanted humanity for long centuries! He was no classical hero, wresting the secrets of life from a reluctant and capricious fate. On the one hand he had his particular brand of religious dogma by which he lived as a good—if unpopular—preacher. And on the other hand he had an elegant experiment involving the focussing of

2

a burning glass on mercuric oxide, leading to the release of what was later called oxygen. The experiment was in its way as ingeniously designed as the trick by which a named card is caused to rise unaided from a wine glass. But—and this is an important point—Priestley's experiment produced a result that was quite new to knowledge. And much more important still, the new information coming out of the demonstration with the burning glass at once enabled the lively mind of Lavoisier in Paris to see how a whole series of other observations fitted together to make an intellectually satisfactory hypothesis not only to explain combustion but to explain breathing as well.

There are text-books galore to teach schoolchildren about the burning glass and the mercuric oxide. The details of the way the experiment was done are all very well for people who like such things. What, to my mind, however, is *really* important and exciting is that—by the use of his intellect—the scientist produces a logical and completely materialistic explanation not only of fire but of the breath of life as well! I discuss this further in Chapters 11 and 12 of this book.

The basic reason why what is described as science is so incomprehensible to the ordinary layman is that most of the scientists themselves, although they may understand the technical words of which their gospel is made up, do not understand the implications of the text as a whole. They are, one might suggest, in the same condition as educated chimpanzees who have been taught to hammer out English words on the typewriter. It would be nice to believe that the laws of probability were such that if a whole thousand of them only played long enough on a thousand machines, they would eventually be found to have typed out the complete works of Shakespeare. But we also know that even if they were spared sufficiently long to complete this considerable task, none of them would have much idea what Shakespeare was about.

Priestley, great experimenter though he was, missed the philosophical implication of his discoveries. Of course, others did too. Charles Darwin was a most conscientious adherent of

the Church of England who had no intention whatever of up-
setting the whole background of belief of his own and all
subsequent generations. Yet his researches as a biologist,
published in *The Origin of Species*, appeared to many devout
people to overthrow the teachings of the first chapters of the
Book of Genesis. If these big men failed to appreciate to what
extent the implications of their scientific observations were
changing the whole complexion of the thought of their times,
may we not excuse those of smaller stature for missing the
meaning of what science is about. Today there are large
numbers of men and women who earn their living at scientific
pursuits. Many of these do research, make minor discoveries
and publish their results in the scientific literature. It is from the
gradual accumulation of laborious detailed observations of new
facts that the fewer greater men may discern a new general
principle by which science may in truth make a stride forward.
Most of the many diligent people do their jobs as research
workers as well as the rank and file of other professions. But
this is not to say that they always appreciate what science is.
Furthermore, as the mass of detailed information increases, it
becomes more and more technical. Technical words have consequently to be invented to describe the increasingly detailed
mechanisms with which professional scientists are dealing.
Inevitably these technical words are incomprehensible to ordinary people. And since many of those who work in the laboratories do not really know why they are doing what they are
and have *never* known that science is anything more than the
massing of more and more of this particular kind of information, it is hardly surprising that the whole thing becomes
impenetrably obscure to the laity.

The philosophy of science by which we conduct the material
affairs of our lives today says three important things. Firstly,
it says that a scientist may enquire about anything. Its second
essential feature is that the results of its enquiries must be
recorded and, as soon as a way has been found to do so, recorded in quantitative terms as weights, measurements, wave-

lengths, velocities, temperatures, chemical composition, atomic configuration—or what you will. The third tenet of science is that, basing his conclusions on the recorded observations, the scientist can set up a theory or hypothesis to explain the facts he has observed and measured. If he can devise an experiment dependent on his hypothesis and the results of this experiment come out as they should, then he can be more confident that the hypothesis is correct.

But this philosophy has one or two uncomfortable consequences for people who are prepared to face it squarely. It is, of course, an *intellectual* philosophy! We have gradually come to accept scientific conclusions for certain aspects of our lives. We expect logical and systematic researches to be carried out to develop new drugs and antiseptics. We accept radar and polythene plastics and we expect engineers to apply the scientific principles of thermodynamics to the calculation of the steam requirements of a new factory design. But this logical, rational behaviour at times comes into collision with illogical 'human' behaviour. Science, that is, with its conclusions based on facts must inevitably be affronted by traditions based on emotion or perhaps on prejudice. We exhibit a split-personality when, as a nation in a scientific age, we build new aeroplanes containing every technical refinement scientific discovery can suggest and at the same time build new houses with water-pipes running down the outside walls where each winter they freeze up and burst.

Just as science may ask questions about traditional housebuilding, so also could it study the statement, 'democracy is the most satisfactory form of government'. This is for us a tribal assumption at the present time, but it is by no means impossible to subject it to scientific scrutiny. This could be done, for example, by comparing a series of factors selected to indicate happiness, prosperity, freedom from criminal activities, educational levels and so on in broadly comparable countries governed under democratic and under non-democratic systems. Of course, we do not in practice do this sort of thing with science. As I said before, we apply the scientific philosophy only to the material things of life. By restricting it thus we sometimes get into trouble. Our electric bells ring very loudly and our jet planes travel very fast—but we are occasionally at something of a loss to know what to do with ourselves when the planes have taken us to wherever it is they are going.

Nevertheless, we are compelled most gratefully to admit that science is wonderful! We have restricted it to the material plane and on that plane it has given us some remarkable things. And the number and variety of these scientific products constantly increases. For instance, there are bicycles, motor-cars, steam-engines and aeroplanes. There are telephones, telegraphs, radio and television. There is gaslight or electric light. Castor oil is not a scientific drug, but aspirin is, and so are sulphanilamide and penicillin and insulin and cortisone. Then we have nylon and perspex and bakelite and ball-point pens, all—to varying degrees—scientific products.

In the United States, they call the man who drives a railway engine an engineer. In Great Britain we would only properly call him an engineer if he could design a railway engine as well as drive it. There is some argument, even in Great Britain, as to whether, even if he *could* design a railway engine, the engineer would be properly called a scientist. In current language the engine-driver is a technician and the engineer a technologist. The engineer can at least understand science even though few engineers and no engine drivers, unless they are quite exceptional, can *do* science—that is, advance the boundaries of new knowledge.

It has been said that a 'practical man' is a man who is ignorant of the principles upon which his practice is based. The modern insistence on distinguishing between a technologist (who *does* understand scientific principles) and a technician (who doesn't) shows that we have today realised that a 'practical man' has his limitations. After all, it does not take very long to teach a man born in the jungles of the Congo to handle a combine harvester or an automatic pom-pom anti-aircraft gun, both of which are complex products of scientific technology. Consequently we grade the technologist one stage higher than the technician. The technologist, indeed, is a very important man. Even after he has completed his grammar-school curriculum it will take him at least three years of further education before he is fully trained. But although he is important in our present scientific world, there are two kinds of people who are more important still. The first is the person who can make new use of scientific facts or who can discover new facts for himself. No one can deny that Thomas Edison, who invented whole lists of practical things, including the electric bell and the telephone, has been useful to the world. The work of Nobel, the inventor of dynamite, has had a considerable impact. Stephenson and Watt and a host of others were heroes whose inventions fired the imaginations of our Victorian grandparents.

This is all very exciting, but is it science? In the eyes of the world it is. Or, at least, at its best it is the application of the scientific method. What has happened, however, is that by the very success of the experimental method, by the very proliferation of new facts, the discovery of new ways to make steel, the manufacture from wood shavings of artificial silk— all this has obscured our minds to the philosophy upon which the whole business is based. We must not blame the 'scientist' who has just set up a factory to make coal-tar dyes for being confused as to what the principles behind science are. He is altogether too busy trying to remember the chemical configuration of benzene and phenol and naphthalene and anthracene and what effects temperature and acidity and a variety of catalysts will have. And if he is successful, he will soon be dealing with complex questions of packaging and marketing and sales and profits as well as with all the problems of chemical technology. He may not even remember why it is the people who buy his dye want to colour the things *they* make with the particular colour *he* makes.

The inventors of stainless steel and nylon and jet engines

and cathode tubes for television sets are the second most important people in our scientific world of today. These dedicated men and women are the intellectual welter-weights. To succeed they must devote themselves wholeheartedly to their science. Their training starts young and is prolonged. And they can never afford to break training. It is said in the United States that unless a man applies himself with such unswerving diligence to his subject that he becomes a professor by the age of forty, he has 'had it' and never will become a professor. Under these circumstances, it is not surprising that devotion to business prevents these people from thinking about principle.

The most important people in our present civilisation are few. They are those who not only know some science but who also appreciate what science involves. The jet plane is a fine way of travelling at 2,000 miles an hour and the family motorcar that can achieve 70 is also to be commended. But why does the family want to travel so fast and what will it do with itself when it gets to its destination? Rudyard Kipling once wrote a story about a man who was smitten by an insane desire to travel faster and faster round the world and who spent his whole life in ships and trains feverishly studying timetables to avoid a moment's delay. Eventually, a resourceful friend persuaded him that if he sat in a chair suspended over a sheet of iron, the world would revolve free beneath him and he could circumnavigate the globe in a day without ever moving. There is a distinct danger that we modern urban citizens, with technical resources now much greater than those of Kipling's traveller, may develop the same neurosis.

But the insight of the important people about whom I am writing extends beyond an appreciation of the purpose that drives us to elaborate our mechanical gadgets and extend the numbers of our washing machines and ball-point pens and portable radios and automatic cigarette lighters and patent breakfast foods until we are well-nigh crushed under the weight of them. Their insight can also comprehend the general character of scientific philosophy. That is, that *all* matters without exception can be subjected to scientific scrutiny so long as they can in some way be measured. Because we only apply scientific techniques to certain material things, like coal-tar drugs or radio-activity, it does not mean that this restriction of scope is necessary.

The top grade of scientist, about whom I have been writing, extends his appreciation of the general philosophy of science to the particular aspects of it with which he is concerned in his day-to-day life. The run-of-the-mill research worker is the backbench member of the parliament of science. His recorded observations form the continuous debate that fill the immense Hansard of the overwhelming scientific literature with which investigators have to struggle today. But here and there are the grade-one people who are capable of seeing the under-lying relation between apparently disconnected facts. These are the cabinet ministers who frame the laws. Isaac Newton put order into a mass of miscellaneous facts and produced the laws of motion. Dalton gave us laws of chemical combination. Pasteur established general principles that at one and the same time explained the observed facts of fermentation and opened up a new science of bacteriology that revolutionized the practice of medicine. In our own generation the *principles* underlying the scattered facts of atomic physics and of much of biochemistry—to name but two topics—have been elucid-ated by men and women who saw beyond the immediate ex-periment to the general relationship linking the observations of many experimenters.

There is an even broader aspect of life to which the philo-sophy of science can be applied. But when this territory is reached the scientist must recognise his limitations. It is the common talk of all Public Persons that by science, and by science alone, we can 'raise our standard of living', 'increase our productivity' and generally improve 'output', 'security', 'amenity', and, of course, 'maximise the export drive'. Progress in science, however, is usually assumed to be restricted to the widening of our knowledge of Nature and the application of

9

this knowledge to material things. The *purpose* of our pursuit of science and the influence of scientific thinking on human happiness is usually ignored. The scientific philosophy is a way of attaining the truth about all sorts of things—about the atom of matter, about human health or about the human mind. But it has had nothing to say about the beauty of a rose and very little to say about right behaviour. Yet, as the researches of Darwin in biology and their relation to the Old Testament, or the studies of Margaret Mead in ethnology and their bearing on the marriage customs of the West, show, the rational approach of science must be viewed in the context of the total philosophy by which we guide our actions.

It is instructive to compare something of the philosophy of science in the West with that in China. Since the eighteenth century our practice has been to *apply* scientific knowledge as soon as we have discovered it—or, at least, as soon as we wake up to the fact that the knowledge *has been* discovered and can be applied. And the effect of this philosophical attitude of materialistic dynamism has been to give us our present astonishing world full of *things*. The Chinese, on the other hand, have during their millenniums of history made many discoveries. But for them, the knowledge itself was the important thing, not its possible application to hum-drum affairs. For example, they discovered the magnetic compass; but it was Western mariners who used it for steering ships. They discovered gun-powder and exhibited it in fireworks for rejoicing. We employed it in war as an instrument of politics.

Our philosophy of scientific materialism has, however, been immensely successful. And the speed of advance is accelerating. New machines, new chemicals, new sources of power and their application are being developed more and more quickly. The steam engine held its own for a hundred years, the motor-car for fifty. The propeller-driven aeroplane has been an effective means of transport for only twenty years and is already being superseded. Mass production increased the effectiveness of a single man's work many times, automation is now developing the trend still further. Obviously, we are proceeding towards our goal at a very rapid pace.

But what is our goal? What is the educated, sane man doing in the world of science? Joseph Priestley was peculiarly gifted, not only with religious belief and scientific genius, but also because he enjoyed doing his writing surrounded by his young children, his wife and all the hurly-burly of noisy family life. In our own crowded century we too live surrounded by the noises of our generation—the underground trains, the helicopters overhead, the voices from the television and from the successive strident editions of the evening papers. There is nothing, I suppose, to stop the sane man living a sane human life in this sort of world, provided he has the strength of mind to do so.

There are occasions when we fail to conduct ourselves sensibly in the midst of all our scientific and technological successes. Sometimes we fail to remember that science, no matter how technical and obscure its terminology may be, is after all only a logical marshalling of natural facts. It is unreasonable to expect that a layman can know all the facts of all the sciences. We do not pretend to understand in detail how a modern motor-car works unless we are motor mechanics, but at least we know that it cannot fly or answer the telephone. On the other hand intelligent laymen, unaware of the basis of science, are prepared to believe that equally impossible things can be done if only they are wrapped up in pseudo-scientific jargon. A few chapters of this book cite examples of this unfortunate credulity and of the paraphernalia that helps to make it acceptable. But having dealt with this, we should consider some of the new things that are happening to justify our pride in the remarkable new achievements of science at this very moment. Besides seven-league strides in mechanical sciences, equally important advances are taking place in the biological sciences and these also we shall consider.

In other chapters something of the facts of this science that affects our lives at every point must be reviewed to see how they affect the philosophy by which we live. Is scientific materialism a good philosophy? Does our growing knowledge of biological science throw any illumination on technological materialism? When automation makes all the things we want and does all our drudgery as well, shall we change for the better or the worse?

Of course, we cannot hope to give final answers to these questions. But, as the White King so aptly said, 'There's nothing like eating hay when you're faint.' He did not say that there was nothing better, but that there was nothing *like* it. And we also can agree that there's nothing like science.

# HUMBUG IN SCIENCE

SCIENCE, with all its great material successes to its credit, has become today an important way of thought. It is indeed probably the most important intellectual influence in our modern philosophy. There is a danger, therefore, that it may tend to be taken too solemnly, too uncritically. Science, as we have said, is the precise assessment and collation of facts. Any conclusions drawn from these facts must be verifiable by experiment. But one thing which has been unduly neglected by scientists is the old question as to whether a tree that falls in the desert makes any noise when nobody is there to hear it. And this is odd because it was Einstein, the greatest of them all, who pointed out that any particular scientist was mistaken in assuming that two things happened simultaneously in two different places when he could never be in two places at once to see both things happening. Einstein, in fact, suggested in his polite mathematics, which were mercifully incomprehensible not only to lay people but to most scientists as well, that confident scientific assumptions such as these might be humbug. Quite recently, however, there is some evidence that the tide of scientific solemnity is turning. One or two papers have appeared in the literature in which humbug is seriously discussed. And it may not be long before it is recognised that humbug plays an important role in certain branches of science.

When a research worker sets out systematically to discover whether vitamin tablets—let us say—prevent your catching cold, it is no good his giving them to a group of people throughout the winter and asking them at the end whether they have had fewer colds than during the year before. Neither is it enough to give vitamins to half the people in a large group and compare them with the other half who are given nothing. The power of the mind over the body is such that some of the people receiving the pills will be affected one way or the other by the very fact that *something* is being done to them. This being so, the competent experimenter is now trained to give vitamin tablets, or whatever it is he may be testing, to one group of people and dummy tablets to another exactly comparable group. The dummy pills are commonly termed, in the technical vernacular, 'placebos'.

Until lately little attention has been paid to the nature of the placebo itself. Provided that it was inert, that was all that mattered. This is now changed. Although describing it as a 'humble humbug', a writer in a recent number of the *Transactions of the College of Physicians of Philadelphia* pointed out the necessity of close scientific study being made of the placebo, now dignified with the title of a 'research tool'. Another writer in the *American Journal of Medicine* goes into some detail on the matter. He considers that when humbug is required for scientific purposes it should be efficient. A placebo medicine should, it now appears, be red, yellow or brown, *not* blue or green, which are colours associated with liniments or poisons. The taste should be bitter but not unpleasant. Capsules or tablets should be coloured and either very small—implying that they are excessively potent—or impressively large; and they should not look like everyday things such as aspirin.

Just as Einstein's events which happen in two places at once may be influenced by the person who observes them, so, it is now argued, a particular drug cannot, in a scientific sense, be said to have a particular effect on any organ of the body without taking into account the personality of the man or woman to whom the body belongs. The *Journal of Pharmacology* published a learned article not long ago pointing out that when a drug is being tested for its effect, let us say, on the pain from wounds, as is only right and proper, half of the group of patients are injected with an inert placebo—usually salt and water. It is nearly always found that some of these patients report that the placebo has relieved their pain. A scientific study of these 'placebo reactors', as they are called, shows that, like people who are 'accident prone', they possess certain characteristics. These people who are particularly susceptible to humbug, we must assume, are more grateful to the doctors who are experimenting on them, more co-operative with the nurses, and more talkative than 'normal' individuals.

As soon as one starts to investigate humbug in science, it is surprising how many scientists one discovers whose whole lives are devoted to the subject. The 'meat cutlet' of the vegetarian restaurant, complete with its paper frill round its artificial 'bone' of uncooked macaroni, is achieved without the aid of science, but the whole army of chemists busy fabricating artificial cream, or artificial colours simulating egg in cake or oak smoke in kippers, or artificial egg albumen for baking are all engaged in harnessing scientific knowledge to the humbug business.

When we discuss the shortage of scientific manpower which is hampering the full development of this country in a competitive world, it is salutary to recall that highly qualified colloid chemists are devoting their talents and the fruits of prolonged training and education to such problems as the best method to prevent the orange pulp in orange squash settling to the bottom of the bottle. In the field of brewing, a great research foundation has been established one of whose major preoccupations is to prevent beer from becoming cloudy. Not long ago, when beer was consumed from pewter vessels, science would have been relieved of the pursuit of this piece of amiable humbug.

The scientific problems which arise in the study of the humbug demanded by modern fancy are very real ones. No one has ever been known to contract a disease from a loaf of bread which is handled with reasonable care. But today, just as our Victorian grandmothers used to avoid the improper sight of uncovered legs—*any* kind of legs—by affixing little skirts to the legs of dining-room tables, so do we eschew the sight of uncovered food by insisting that bread be wrapped. This innocent desire sets the research chemists several difficult conundrums. Microbiologists must be employed to study the types of mould which tend to develop inside the wrapping paper. Organic chemists are required to investigate possible antimycotic agents which could prevent the moulds from growing. Cereal chemists must be engaged to research into the nature of crumb toughness.

To the scientist, the nature of the problem is everything. The purpose for which the work is done is very little. He will work with as much devotion to perfect a colour or a varnish so that a new model of a motor-car can claim to be the 'most beautiful object on four wheels' as he will to invent a new anaesthetic. And this is right and proper, for who knows what may be the ultimate outcome of a scientific investigation?

Humbug, however, can come into science in a different and less attractive form. For example, a few years ago two young men who were engaged in an investigation into the composition of wool discovered a new method of analysis. Such a discovery is of fundamental importance in science since progress is often brought to a halt by the inability of classical analytical methods to separate chemical substances of distinct but similar nature. The technique invented by these two young men, Drs Martin and Synge, for which, very appropriately, they were awarded a Nobel Prize, was sublimely simple as so many strokes of genius often are. Its principle was as follows. If you drop red ink on to blotting-paper the mixed pigments in the ink separate into their different colours as the blot expands. In the same way, if a mixture of, say, the different sugars that occur naturally in honey are allowed to spread slowly down a strip of blotting-paper they also will separate out and the quantities of the individual sugar-types can be measured. The original form of the process consisted of hanging a long wet strip of paper overnight in a container which kept the atmosphere moist. In the learned paper announcing the discovery to a meeting of the Biochemical Society, the inventors described how they used lengths of earthenware drainpipe for the purpose. Nowadays, although lots of chemists still use equally simple apparatus for this work, there are on the market elaborate and expensive vessels fitted with all kinds of gadgets for carrying out 'paper-partition chromatography'. In fact these elegant pieces of apparatus, although sometimes more convenient than the old-fashioned drainpipes, do the same job. And there are research workers who try them. The scientist, after all, is only a man. He needs constantly to be kept awake to reality if he is not to forget that this type of thing, together with the chromium-plated taps you turn on with your feet, may in fact be nothing but humbug.

Another bit of humbug in science is found with the use of a special language. There is no harm in this of itself; indeed, much of science is so complicated that the employment of a specialised jargon, the words of which possess a precise technical meaning, is of convenience as a species of shorthand. But there are occasions when technical language is used to make something that is, in fact, simple and commonplace sound as if it were important and learned. For example, to an ordinary person 'literature' is a written record of something worth saying, well said. To a scientist, however, 'the literature' is anything at all, important or unimportant, that has appeared in a technical journal about the subject under discussion. And in this 'literature' the scientist may wrap himself up and hide himself away from reality in the liturgy of a ritual passive voice. Oddly enough, he is compelled to use this grammatical

17

form by the insistence of scientific editors. But if he were
allowed to write straight down what he had done, without
humbug, he might not publish any report until he really *had*
made a discovery. As it is, we get this sort of thing:

> The test was made immediately after *the subjects* had con-
> sumed meals, the solid portions of which varied from 6 to
> 18 oz. From the results *it was found that* the effect of size of
> meal on number of words typed was *highly significant*, the
> typist working best after meals, the portions of which
> weighed 9 to 12 oz. However, in *further tests it was found*
> that the effect of size of meal was rendered insignificant if
> *motivation* to do well were sufficiently great.

In other words, the scientific nutrition of one's typist helps
her with her work—unless it doesn't.

Throughout the whole period of his academic training the
scientist is gradually conditioned by the language of his text-
books as well as by the kind of prose favoured by the editorial
boards of learned journals to use long, pompous, Latin words
when he could use short Anglo-Saxon ones. The phrases to be
found in his illiterate 'literature' are usually long and involved
rather than short and pithy. Dr Johnson illustrated the effect
of this way of writing. In English, the sentence is: 'It has
not wit to keep it sweet.' With the assistance of Latinised
words this becomes: 'It has not vitality to preserve it from
putrefaction.'

Not long ago, R. Whitehead writing in the *Lancet* pointed
out that scientists when they meant 'say' would try to make
their statements seem more impressive by using 'affirm',
'allege', 'assert', 'aver', 'claim', 'contend', 'declare', 'intimate',
'maintain', or 'state' instead. Surely, this is humbug. Instead of
'much', they write 'a considerable amount of', 'a great deal of',
'a large proportion of', or 'quite a large quantity of' and their
prose is peppered with such phrases as 'circular in outline',
'complex in character', 'large in size', 'next in order', and most
popular of all, 'red in colour'.

This brings me to a difficult and important aspect of humbug in science. The question whether a modern scientist is an educated man. For a long time it has been thought that only a liberal knowledge of the classics justified a man considering himself to be an educated person in the full sense. Such an education gave him an understanding of men and affairs, of literature and philosophy, and of the languages and customs of countries other than his own. In recent years, Cabinet Ministers, senior Civil Servants and other Powerful People have begun to realise that science could achieve material results unattainable otherwise. The detonation of the first atomic bomb really brought home the fact that scientists were, at least on this striking material plane, to be reckoned with. Consequently, those in positions of authority were not entirely unwilling to be convinced by the argument put forward by scientists with increasing assurance that a 'scientific training' was, in fact, a liberal education.

It is difficult to assert, in the face of the great and increasing mass of technical publications printed each year, that a scientific education, as at present administered, conduces to much elegance in literary style. Once upon a time it was the custom for scientific workers to move about and study in other countries. Most of the older generation of scientists used to work for a period in a German laboratory. A vestigial remnant of this internationalism remains in the British practice of setting chemists an examination in German translation. But this is now recognised to be of no cultural significance and few English-speaking chemists can do better than scramble through a German technical paper with a dictionary as a crutch.

We must face the fact that in the practical world of affairs science is not accepted as a philosophy but as a way of doing things. A scientific education is designed to teach the student the factual knowledge to enable him to handle chemicals or electrical apparatus or machinery in its various sorts. The illiterate scientists, it must be admitted, are many, the scientific philosophers are few. Sometimes, in the hope that the assertion is true and not humbug, that scientific education fits a man for the affairs of the world, the research worker is brought from his back room and taken into the boardroom. There he sits in barely concealed boredom while general matters are being discussed. Only when his own items are reached in the agenda does he hold forth, *ex cathedra*—and then stops.

The study of Latin verbs or Greek syntax cannot of itself be claimed to furnish the mind with much else than a set of more or less arbitrary rules. But the *Odyssey* (as has been shown by the enormous sales of the Penguin translation) by reporting the behaviour and feelings of men three thousand years ago gives us ideas to guide our own behaviour today. The modern teaching of chemistry and physics and mechanics produces a competent technologist. Sometimes it produces a scientist. But if it produces a philosopher this is quite accidental. The contribution of science has been the thesis that logical study, experimentation and the acceptance of conclusions based on fact no matter how unexpected or unpalatable are the way to truth. Scientific education teaches its pupils to apply these principles only to material things. Until the philosophy with all its implications is taught as applying also to government, social affairs, even religion itself perhaps, there surely is an element of humbug in claiming that the study of 'science' as we understand the word produces educated men.

One more piece of humbug might be included here: the belief that the scientist, the dedicated research worker, does his job to benefit humanity. This extraordinary delusion is held to apply most directly to scientific persons involved in medical matters. There are in hospitals whole laboratories full of scientifically trained men and women, all busily engaged in matching blood samples, analysing what are euphemistically called 'specimens', looking at slices of flesh under microscopes and carrying out the whole complex programme of the tests that prudent doctors demand, not necessarily to help the patients, but to protect their attendants from subsequent legal action if, as is bound to occur eventually in this mortal scene, the patient does not recover. These scientists do their jobs as well as anybody else, but the measure of service to humanity in their work is no greater than that of motor mechanics.

Dr L. W. Batten in the course of a lecture to the final-year medical students at St Bartholomew's Hospital, London, pointed out that, although modern medicine depends on science and the continuing work of scientists, the practice of medicine is an art. He also pointed out that all artists work partly for money. Shakespeare wrote his plays, Bach composed his Brandenburg concertos, Michelangelo got his David out of that lump of marble—partly for money; although none of them got very rich. The popular impression of a doctor selflessly serving suffering humanity is exaggerated. Good doctors, says Dr Batten, are seldom dedicated to the service of humanity. Partly, like the rest of us, they work for money and partly they work for the praise of their peers. But though they do not say so, the best of them are dedicated to the practice of medicine. That is to say, they are interested in their work.

It is as unreasonable to single out the doctors and nurses for special gratitude for scientific activity on behalf of suffering mankind, merely because we see them actually dealing with sufferers, as it is to tip the waiter but not the cook or the kitchen maid when we go to a restaurant. Louis Pasteur was applying his chemical acumen to preventing wine going sour when he developed the discovery that solved the problem of infectious disease. Service to suffering humanity did not come into it. The scientist who did more to earn the gratitude of suffering humanity than a complete Royal-College-full of medical consultants was the engineer who thought out the process for making iron pipes and thus enabled us to keep the sewage separate from the drinking water. It was this scientific advance that rendered possible the great populous cities that we find necessary for our happiness today.

The popular imagination is strange and unpredictable. It is traditional folk-lore of our time to think of a civil servant as a dried-up sort of fellow with a rolled umbrella and a well developed contempt for the ordinary citizen, who arrives at his office late in the morning, continuously drinks cups of tea while he is there and enjoys six weeks' holidays plus six weeks' sick leave every year. Yet a civil servant is far more directly concerned with benefiting humanity than a scientist. He often has to think about humanity—or at least about that section of it with which he is employed to deal. A scientist engaged, let us say, by a great chemical company may be far removed from any thoughts of humanity, suffering or otherwise. Yet, just as it was said of McCormack that his invention of the mechanical reaper straightened the bent backs of the peasants of the world, so equally could it be held that the anonymous inventors of nylon allowed the weary housewives of at least a substantial proportion of the world to put down their darning needles. But it is clearly humbug to believe that the research team that made the discovery, and the chemical engineers and administrators who made the nylon, and the investors and boards of directors and shareholders who made it possible for the manufacture to take place at all were impelled by altruistic notions about the sufferings of mankind.

Thus we see that although science is a potent means of making material things, of creating power and of controlling Nature and, most important of all, is the dominant philosophy by which our Western technology is directed, nevertheless humbug enters into its operation in a number of ways. Humbug is a necessary and useful feature in the 'controls' used to measure the effectiveness of new drugs and new vitamins, the very existence of which it would sometimes be impossible to establish without it. But humbug in science has only a limited function for good. Usually it is bad because it is by its very nature false, and the core of science is truth. Elaborate and unnecessarily complex apparatus designed to impress rather than to enlighten is a hindrance to discovery. There is the sad story from the United States of a first-rate scientist who was studying the nature of the proteins in blood plasma. For part of his research he needed to use a machine called an 'ultracentrifuge'. This is a large, complicated and very expensive piece of equipment which separates substances suspended in liquid by spinning a test tube full of the mixture at extremely high speed. His studies yielded interesting results which were published. But instead of being able to proceed with the next logical step in his intricate research he found himself bombarded with samples of blood plasma from other doctors all over the place who had half-understood the significance of his published report. They had the idea that his kind of studies *might* be useful for some of their patients. But above all, they were impressed by his expensive and unusual apparatus. When last heard of he was set up in a big office in an institute with *four* ultra-centrifuges, so bombarded with miscellaneous blood samples as to have no time left to think or to carry out new research.

The adaptability of the modern citizen to the stresses of the crowded world in which he is subjected to all sorts of scientific marvels is remarkable. He quickly tends to develop, to a greater or lesser degree, a protective armour against a good deal of the humbug by which he is assailed. The scientist also must in his professional life defend himself against the same influences. Sometimes he needs to use humbug as part of his science. Usually, however, he needs to be on the defensive against the special dangers of pompous and obscure language, of woolly, grandiose thoughts about the cultural significance of his activities, of windy beliefs in his mission in the world, or, most dangerous of all, of coming to believe his own humbug.

# 3

# THE COMIC ELEMENT

In its earlier days, science was a constant butt for people who wanted to make fun of it. Perhaps even the story of Icarus who tried to fly up to the sun until his wax wings melted and he was dashed to the ground has an element of the comic about it. Nowadays, of course, aeronautics is a serious matter of science. The shape of wings and the materials of their construction are matters for calculation and analysis. We can today all talk technically about the sound barrier and Mach numbers. The thought that a man can stand up and shout and then get into a machine and overtake his own voice does not strike us as strange at all. Preparations for the International Geophysical Year proceeded as unconcernedly and with as much dullness as preparations for an international trade fair at an industrial town in the Midlands. But surely there is something of the comic in the fact that the ten artificial moons, ordered by the United States Defence Department from a firm in Baltimore with as little fuss as if they had been railway locomotives, are being launched from Banana River, Florida.

We all know that the design of 'earth satellites' is a great stride forward in technological achievement. But is there not something comic—or is it merely grotesque—in the report of the U.S. Air Force Aero-Medical Laboratory at Dayton, Ohio, on the physiological effects of space flight? Moses, you will remember, when controlling the migration of the Israelites through the wilderness, sent out spies into Canaan. The initial report of these men was an unfavourable one and only one eventually survived to reach the new country. Today, in our modern scientific context, we also have sent off spies into the promised land of outer space. Five monkeys were despatched in an *Aerobee* rocket. This machine flew up seventy miles high but on returning to earth four of the monkeys were killed when their parachutes failed to open. The single survivor of these simian heralds of humanity landed safely but died of heat and thirst in the wilderness of New Mexico before help arrived.

The way scientists restrict their thinking to material things has for a long time been considered comic by non-scientific people. Swift, in *Gulliver's Travels*, imagines scientists wandering about with their thoughts on their experiments, each requiring the attendance of a servant to attract his attention to everyday affairs by hitting him with a balloon. During the Victorian age it was still quite the fashion to crack jokes about science and scientists. Mr Pickwick is an obvious example, with his scientific study of tittlebats in the ponds of Hampstead and Highgate. But nowadays science, the visible sign of our present greatness and the only hope of an existence in the future, is a solemn subject.

And yet there is a comic aspect of present-day science: and it is often provided by the scientist himself.

For example, there is something just a trifle bizarre in the thought of three German scientists devoting themselves to study, and publishing a report entitled, 'The nutritive value of St John's-wort for swine', when their findings were that St John's-wort has no nutritive value for swine. Researches on 'The sintering of fly-ash', or a study of twelve kinds of plaster of Paris written by two Japanese gentlemen at Tohoku University, are obviously useful contributions to knowledge. But perhaps, as he passes on his way through the quiet corridors of Tohoku University, one of the older teachers may allow himself to smile. Plaster of Paris *seems* such an odd topic to devote one's thoughts to at a university.

The absent-minded professor is a traditional figure of fun. Long may he remain so. The world is full of serious matters and among the most serious are, unfortunately, many of us modern scientists who have no time to remember that science is a philosophy of men seeking truth. In a more leisurely age, fashionable crowds used to flock to the Royal Institution to enjoy elegant demonstrations of science—of electricity, or laughing gas, or astronomy. Nowadays, much of science is strictly utilitarian. Many scientists are, perforce, employees. For them, science is a means of making *things*—plastics, chemicals, alloys, plaster of Paris, or explosives. Unfortunately, these are not for elegant entertainment but for sale or for some utilitarian purpose. The Gods may justly laugh at the diligent, scientific blind men forever working away at their fly-ash (whatever that may be), too many times without thought of the structure of matter itself, or of systems of behaviour for civilised men.

But apart from the wryly humorous aspects of the doings of the scientists, there is a curiously comic element in science itself.

Let me give some examples from biochemistry. Certain foods, among which sweetbreads are probably the most prominent, contain nitrogenous components called purines. These are degraded during the process of digestion. Man and anthropoid apes excrete purines in the form of a well-known chemical substance, uric acid. All other mammals—with one exception—excrete them from the body in the form of a substance called allantoin. Birds behave differently from these lower mammals and excrete their purines in the form of uric acid. There is a good biochemical reason for the choice of uric acid by birds. It arises from the fact that they live an appreciable proportion of their lives shut up in an egg-shell. Many of

the nitrogenous excretion products used by mammals are toxic
and must be got rid of immediately. If these were produced by
the chicken in its egg-shell they would poison it. Uric acid,
however, as is well known by sufferers from gout, is highly
insoluble. It consequently crystallises out from the circulating
fluids of the chick and allows the young bird to dispose of its
surplus nitrogenous breakdown-products without harm to itself.

Now, as I have said, other than man and the higher apes
all mammals—with *one* exception—excrete the nitrogenous
purines as allantoin; the exception is the Dalmatian coach-
hound; it excretes uric acid like a bird. Surely, there is something just slightly comic in this animal, of all others, having
been singled out for such a curious distinction. And the impersonal diligence of scientific research has further enriched the
point. A detailed biochemical study was carried out in the
United States at the kennels of a dog fancier who had devoted
considerable effort to breeding thoroughbred Dalmatian coach-
hounds specially trained to run under the back axles of buggies.
During the course of this investigation it emerged that only
certain dogs could be taught to run properly under back axles.
These were the pure-bred Dalmatians. If the line was sullied
to the least degree the capacity was lost. Perhaps most remarkable of all was the fact that the ability to learn was also related
to the capacity to perform the unique mammalian biochemical
anomaly, namely, to excrete uric acid instead of allantoin. The
title of the paper enshrining this scientific fact is 'Biochemical
factors related to the learning ability of Dalmatian coach-
hounds'.

One of the great comic conceptions of literature is that of
Don Quixote and the notion of someone continuing to pursue
a fixed idea—a fixed scale of values—no matter how in-
appropriate the time or circumstance has been accepted as
comic for the last three hundred years. The fact that the idea
in this story was a serious one has not detracted from the comic
element of the narrative. The behaviour of the insect *Rhodnius
prolixus* might be accepted as equally comic in the scientific

sphere. *Rhodnius prolixus* lives by sucking blood. It only eats occasionally, but when it does it takes a full meal. The effect of the distension of its stomach is to cause a gland in its head to produce a chemical hormone. The discharge of this hormone sets in train a series of reactions which twenty-one days later cause the insect to shed its skin. It has been shown by Dr Wigglesworth of the London School of Hygiene and Tropical Medicine that seven days are required for this sequence of events to be set in motion. He proved this point in the following somewhat bizarre manner. After one of the insects had had its meal, he cut off its head. He kept the body alive for the necessary twenty-one days but the skin was not shed because the gland containing the necessary hormone had been taken away with the missing head. A second insect was given *its* feed of blood and was left for seven days with its head on, after which time it was also decapitated; and within fourteen days the surviving body of this insect shed its skin. The quixotic determination of *Rhodnius prolixus* to adhere to its scientific principles no matter how unpropitious the circumstances is demonstrated in the ultimate experiment. Two insects were taken. The first was fed, left seven days and then had its head cut off. Then the second received *its* meal, and was instantly executed. The two were then joined together. The train of biochemical events set going in the first was so powerful that fourteen days later *both* shed their skins. To many people Don Quixote is not comic. He certainly is not funny. There is, indeed, much of nobility and virtue in his example. Perhaps then the case of *Rhodnius prolixus* playing out its biological purpose regardless of interference by a human experimenter ought to fill us with reverence rather than laughter.

But of course the basic principle of the comic genius is that pride goes before a fall. Literature is full of examples: Shakespeare's Malvolio made to go cross-gartered; Kipling's schoolmaster, Mr Prout, mistaken for a poacher; Anstey's Mr Bultitude suffering the humiliation of being turned into a schoolboy. Or, at its lowest denomination, the pompous citizen stepping on a banana skin. The march of modern science has been so sure, so consequential, that no common mortal would be surprised if a quirk of circumstance pricked one or two of the bubbles. And here and there, the progress of science engineers something comic in this vein, or so it seems to me.

Mrs Beeton advised the mother who is unable to feed her own baby or to obtain a wet nurse to do it for her to use asses' milk. But ever since the second decade of the present century the march of nutritional science has been progressing at an ever-increasing pace. Balanced diets, appropriately charged with vitamins, mineral salts and protein, enable children to grow larger and larger quicker and quicker. Let it not be thought that I would for a moment belittle the massive triumphs of this newer knowledge of nutrition—the virtual disappearance of rickets and of infantile scurvy, for example— but is there not a tiny sting in the tail now apparent—a delicate joke on the part of fate?

Dr Clive McCay of Cornell first showed that if you lavished on rats all the available knowledge of nutrition, you could indeed cause them to grow as quickly and proportionally as big and healthy as modern children. But if, on the other hand, you fed them less well, if, indeed, you gave them from time to time in early life too little to eat, they grew more slowly, it is true, but they lived longer. Now children are not rats; nevertheless Professor McCance of Cambridge has recently pointed out that by raising the plane of nutrition of underfed children, one could in one calendar year increase by two years the physiological age of their bones. It may be, therefore, that when with our scientific nutrition we induce the maximum rate of growth in our children, at the same time we shorten their lives. Clive McCay points out that by a statistical study in London in 1842 Edmunds arrived at the conclusion that longevity was best assured by alternative periods of privation and plenty in early life and, what is more, he published the fact in a monograph entitled: 'Life Tables founded upon the Discovery of a Numerical Law regulating the Existence of Every Human

Being illustrated by a New Theory of the Cause producing Health and Longevity'.

In this solemn twentieth century the purpose of women is to raise industrial productivity. A new Lysistrata, exhorting the sisterhood to strike, would find that she had brought to heel, not husbands, but merely the Chief Conciliation Officer of the Ministry of Labour. Little wonder that we usually consider science to be something serious. A hundred years ago, however, Professor De Morgan, the first professor of mathematics of the then new University of London, thought that there was a good deal of fun in it. In 1872 he published a book called *A Budget of Paradoxes* in which he expended a very sharp wit on all sorts of scientific philosophers who were not necessarily wrong but whose ideas were different from the beliefs of orthodox people.

A hundred years ago men were still prepared to apply scientific methods of thought to ideas in general. In our own age we consider it an orthodox scientific procedure to use science to develop a *machine* for communicating ideas from one person to another. The telephone was one of the first marvels of applied science. We brought the accrued knowledge of electricity and magnetism to bear in order to develop the mechanism. But the scientific snail instantly drew in its horns before the problem of applying logical experimental thought to what we were to say into the telephone. More recently the philosophy of science has given us even more potent machines to transmit our thoughts. We have radio to transmit speech and cathode-ray tubes to transmit optical if not intellectual vision. The electronic computer is yet another scientific *thing* that the materialist philosophy of the age is providing. This tool can be applied to the mechanical translation of languages.

In earlier times, before materialism came down like a shutter to focus the light of science into a single channel of thought, people could be found who did consider how scientific methods might be applied to the transmission of ideas. One of these, selected by Professor De Morgan as an example of a 'paradoxer', was John Wilkins.

Wilkins was one of the men who contributed greatly towards founding the Royal Society of London. He afterwards became Bishop of Chester. In 1668 he published a notion for transmitting thought by a logical method far superior to Esperanto as a universal scientific language. His idea was that things and their relations to each other should be denoted by signs not words. This would allow any person, whatever his mother tongue, to read in his own words. Professor De Morgan commenting on the notion says, 'This is an obvious possibility and, I am afraid, an obvious impracticability. One man may construct such a system—indeed Bishop Wilkins has done it—but where is the man who will learn it?'

Anyone who has attended an international conference today where, even with the aid of interpreters and microphones, progress is reduced to a snail's pace because translations have to be made into half a dozen different languages, could wish that Bishop Wilkins' paradoxical idea of three hundred years ago had been put into effect.

French logic at the end of the eighteenth century began to introduce scientific philosophy into mundane affairs. It is heartening to think of the diligent scientific men measuring a meridian right across France in the turmoil of revolution simply in order to establish the precise length of the standard kilometre upon which all units of length and mass were to be based. The English, however, with their peerless gift for keeping different topics in different closed compartments of their minds, had firmly decided to restrict science solely to the manufacture of steel and sulphuric acid and cotton spinning machinery. On July 12th, 1855, the House of Commons was debating the introduction of decimal coinage. Needless to say, this threatened intrusion of scientific logic into the British garden of illogical units, where stones and gills, furlongs and proof gallons jostle with bushels, several varieties of quarters, drachms, chains, knots, long tons, baskets and quires for the title of principal lord of confusion and error, was easily repelled.

A book called *The Decimal System as a Whole* was published

in the following year, 1856, by a Mr Statter, about which Professor De Morgan wrote, 'the proposition is to make everything decimal. The day, now twenty-four hours, is to be made ten hours. The year is to have ten months, Unober, Duober, etc. Fortunately there are ten commandments, so there will be neither addition to, nor deduction from, the moral law. But the twelve apostles! Even rejecting Judas, there is a whole apostle of difficulty. These points the author does not touch.'

We laugh, perhaps a little sadly, at the savant described by Saki who announced his great discovery of having elaborated a method of communicating human speech to animals, 'like the angel Gabriel announcing the Day of Judgment only to be told that it clashed with Henley and would have to be indefinitely postponed'. Poor Mr Statter! Poor us!

The three blind men describing the elephant—he at the trunk end, as a snake; he handling the leg, as a tree; and he at the tail, as a handful of wires—are a different form of comic invention. They well represent very many of us scientists, however. It is easy to wake up and find that one has spent a lifetime investigating some minor aspect of the chemical configuration of methyl-nor-narcotine, or the club mosses of Kirkcudbright, and be awarded a Ph.D. for the work, without the slightest appreciation of the significance of the study in the context of chemistry or botany or of its application to human affairs. Ernest Thomson Seton once wrote a parable about this kind of researcher. In the deserts of Nevada he came upon a great rock in the shape of a human toe. He stopped and set to work and scraped and polished and wrought until after many years the thing was perfect. He had engraved on it the grain of skin. He had even put a trace of dirt under the nail. And when the thing was done, he died and was buried under the rock. While above him towered the mountain hewn into the mighty shape of a sublime human form by nations long past.

Moses on Sinai in the cleft of the rock and covered by the hand of God was allowed to see God's hinder parts as He passed by. Though he saw little, he knew that what he did see was part of God. The modern scientist has ways of looking into the working of Nature more powerful than anything conceived of in the past, yet he often forgets that what he sees is part of a greater whole.

The history of the advance of science is intertwined with the story of the increasing range and capability of the instruments with which the scientific worker sees the structure and nature of the materials with which he is dealing. These instruments give expression to what is in the mind's eye. Galileo in 1609 suddenly opened the door to the stars by inventing the compound telescope. Almost as an afterthought, he turned the whole thing upside down and invented the microscope as well. Robert Hooke in England, who combined mechanical skill, inventive genius and scientific insight to a remarkable degree, made and used the microscope and, in his *Micrographia*, brought to life a new and unsuspected universe of the very small.

In three hundred years the optical microscope has been improved and from it a tool of a higher order of precision developed, namely, the electron microscope. This instrument is capable of magnifications of the order, in map language, of one inch to the mile, under which conditions a single paint film becomes as thick as the span of a man's hand. With the electron microscope the larger molecules of matter can be seen. Spectroscopic instruments reveal the detailed structure of molecules. Such instruments may use visible light, ultra-violet light, infra-red, X-rays or magnetic resonance. They all reveal to the mind of the scientist vibrations characteristic of the parts of the molecules being inspected. Sometimes it is the carbon skeleton, sometimes the grouping of the atoms and sometimes the whole structure.

There is a further set of tools that enable us to see the very electrons that are the ultimate particles of energy circling within the atoms. In fact, we do not actually see the electrons—only the place where they have been. Much of Lord Rutherford's philosophy was based on the evidence provided by a streak of light across a photographic plate—the path of a particle.

These refined tools and the complex methods by which they are used are of great interest. They are the technical machinery with which science is done. But they are not science. Philosophically an electron microscope or a 50,000-dollar ultracentrifuge is of no more significance to a scientist than the clothes he wears. They enable him to get about among the molecules, but fine feathers no more make fine birds in this business than in any other. The ultimate joke is the sight of one of us diligent modern researchers analysing 716 samples of bath brick and writing a report, with 1,102 references to the literature, entitled, 'A preliminary communication on the sesqui-oxides of silicon as determined by X-ray crystallography with special reference to the Jurassic minerals of central Basingstoke', without a glimmering of any of the general implications behind our immediate occupation. Men like us— and we do exist—are indeed using 'a thousand million candlepower gas microscope of *hextry* power' to see through 'two pair of stairs and a deal door', but we sometimes overlook the fact that our '*wision*' is limited.

# 4

# LIFE AUTOMATIC

THE systematic scientific study of natural phenomena relating
to electricity enabled Michael Faraday and Alessandro Volta
and Ampère (who incidentally showed his intellectual ability
early on by doing abstruse calculations with pebbles at the age
of four) to elucidate principles upon which the technologists
of a later day could base the invention of radio and television.
The philosophy of science thus led to the understanding of
electronics. The effect of this understanding has, however,
affected civilised life in many unexpected ways as we have
already discussed. Broadcasting, a child of science, affects intellectual and cultural aspects of daily life. Scientific developments in our control over mechanical inventions are, however,
going to affect our lives in the material sphere just as much.
The combination of a number of these new inventions and
ideas is today being called 'automation'.

Just over a hundred years ago in 1822, Charles Babbage,
professor of mathematics at Cambridge, bent his mind to the
problem of the nature of calculation. Almost every administrative job that can be thought of is a matter of calculation. The
manager of a factory has to calculate how many cardboard

cartons he will need to cope with next June's output. He must calculate whether if sales went up by $3\frac{1}{2}$ per cent he would need to put on a night shift, and at every stage of his operations he needs to work out his costs. Generals know from bitter experience that success in battle is a matter of the most careful calculation and in up-to-date wars this important fact has been recognised by the establishment of a special section of the general's staff devoted solely to 'logistics'.

Babbage, then, considered the nature of calculation and saw that it fell into three parts. Firstly, there were the processes of multiplying and dividing, which in essentials are merely adding and subtracting. The second part of a calculation is the storing of intermediate results that turn up during the process and thus remembering them until they are needed. And the final operation in a calculation of any complexity is the order in which a sequence of procedures is to be carried out. Babbage, having considered the whole thing scientifically, came to the conclusion that it did not necessarily require a human brain but could be done mechanically. He then sat down and designed a machine that would do what was required. He called it a 'difference engine'. It has a 'mill' capable of multiplying twenty-nine-figure numbers; a store for the intermediate totals; and a control unit that would tell the machine what to do. In actual fact the machine was never built. And even if it had been, it could not possibly have been made to work. The reason for this was that it was perforce designed to be moved mechanically by trains of cogs and its complexity was necessarily such that the conception, though sound, was beyond the reach of the mechanical possibilities of the times.

A somewhat more surprising thing was that Babbage never bothered to publish any clear account of how his computer was planned to work. Parts of it were explained in certain chapters of a diffuse autobiographical work upon which he was engaged, entitled *Passages from the Life of a Philosopher*. In 1824, he gave up his chair at Cambridge and accepted an invitation from some Italian admirers who had been impressed by his originality and mathematical acumen. While he was in Rome, notes were taken of his lectures and these were subsequently published in the Italian language—and then almost completely forgotten. By a somewhat unlikely chance, however, they later came into the hands of Lady Lovelace, the daughter of Lord Byron, who, by an even more improbable coincidence, was an excellent mathematician. She instantly recognised their novelty and importance, translated them back into English and added notes of her own equal to twice the length of the original Italian text. It was from this account that Babbage's son was able actually to make one part of the machine, the 'mill', that is now in the Science Museum in London. More important, however, the report of Babbage's work was the basis for the design of the modern electronic general-purpose computers that can today be made to work electronically, without the need for moving parts.

Although in the world of science thought is very often the prelude to action, and although action based on thought is sometimes of great practical importance—for example, when Pasteur's recognition of the nature of infection enabled us at one and the same time to control infectious diseases *and* run the canning industry—nevertheless, the development of the new idea itself seems to me to be the significant intellectual triumph.

Calculating machines were not entirely new in Babbage's time, although he himself devised significant advances in design. It is, for instance, by no means easy to work out how the machine is to carry numbers forward. But the linking of the 'mill' which can calculate with the 'store' which can remember, and the combining of both with a set of instructions, was new. And from the conception of combining the three operations, a variety of important practical results has arisen. We shall examine first the 'store', the so-called memory of the machine.

One of the simplest mathematical feats is the calculation of a man's wages. All that needs to be done is to multiply the number of hours he has worked at the standard rate of wages by the rate, add on the number of hours of overtime, calculate the income tax, subtract it, add on the shift bonus at the appropriate rate, take off the trade-union dues, the hospital penny-a-week contribution, add on the holiday payment and make an adjustment for under- or over-payment for the previous week. Arithmetically the whole thing is simple. What makes it possible for a computer, however, is its ability to hold in its 'memory' the successive intermediate results while the next operation is being done on them. It can also store from the previous week all the information about wage-rates and bonuses and what the man was paid before. The operation is comparatively simple but the possible practical applications of the machine are many. Just as, in the field of manual labour, the invention of the reaper and binder straightened the bent backs of men and women stooping over the sheaves of grain in the fields, so the electronic computer is straightening the round shoulders of the great battalions of accounts clerks in the office buildings of towns.

Computers can be more or less complicated in construction depending upon the work they are designed to do. A machine for dealing with wages or stock records or for integrating the flow of components on the conveyor belts in a factory need have little ability for mathematics but must have a long memory. On the other hand, a computer intended for the control of a machine tool must possess considerable mathematical ability.

Although in recent times we have become impressed with the cleverness and importance of mass-producing things in large numbers, there is in engineering occasional need to make a small number of things but to make them very well indeed and with a high degree of precision. In mass-production factories, the jigs and tools needed in the process of 'tooling up' or 'retooling' before the production of a new design are examples of these. In aircraft factories the actual aeroplanes themselves are made in small numbers (in comparison with the numbers of motor-cars, for example, coming out of a motor-car factory), yet the accuracy with which their components must be made is high and the shapes of these components are often very difficult to machine. Up till now these special objects have required great skill in their construction and have, in consequence, been expensive. This has partly been due to the difficulty of training machinists capable of doing the work and partly due to the high capital cost of the complex milling machine with which the operation is carried out. Let us for a moment visualise the scene.

A complex aerofoil shape is to be cut from a piece of solid metal composed of an unusual alloy. A careful and experienced operator fits it into the machine, takes a good look at the blueprint and starts up. In a moment or so he stops the machine, refers back to the drawing, checks the work with a calliper gauge and starts up again. After two or three goes like this he comes to a tricky bit on the drawing. He scratches his head for a few minutes, readjusts the machine and starts off again doubtfully. It can be seen that even if all goes well, the output of the extremely expensive tool is very greatly below its potential productivity and entirely because the brain of the man controlling it is too slow. By using an electronic computer and the necessary ancillary gear, this brain work can be mechanised.

It is done like this. A competent mathematician can express any line or curve in the form of an algebraic expression. The aircraft designer, therefore, after having set out the drawing of the part he wants made, expresses the lines of the design in algebraic form—as circles, ellipses, parabolas, hyperbolas or whatever they may be. The instructions given to the computer on a punched tape are therefore that it is to work out the curves of which it has been given the algebraic formulae. This it can, of course, do at very high speed for each of the three dimensions of the solid object that it is desired to make, for that is what this particular computer has been constructed to do. It gives out the answers to the calculations in the form of a stream of pulses on a magnetic tape. This tape goes into the control gear of the milling machine.

The movements of the controlling gear that directs the

milling machine must, of course, be very accurately directed. One ingenious solution to the problem has been to attach what is called an 'optical grating', that is, a transparent strip ruled with great precision with lines extremely close together, to the fixed part of the machine and another to the moving part. These gratings are at a slight angle to each other and as they move a pattern of light is set up. This pattern is converted into electrical pulses by means of photo-electric cells. It is these pulses that fit in with the pulses carrying the instructions from the computer that are sent out by the magnetic tape. So precise is this arrangement that in controlling the movements of the milling machine it can take account of the thickness of an oil film on the metal.

The new scene in the engineering works is now as follows. The designer at his desk has translated his drawing into a list of instructions about which curves and lines he wishes the machine to make. A girl types these instructions as a code on a strip of paper like a teleprinter message. This strip goes into the computer that does the sums and issues the answers as a length of magnetic tape. The tape goes into the milling machine control gear and the machine then gets to work and, without hesitation or delay, without having to stop and scratch *its* head, produces the part it has been told to make. If a second part exactly the same as the first is required, all that is needed is to put the magnetic tape through the automatic controller again. The expensive milling machine can be kept at full stretch the whole time because the thinking required for its control is done automatically. The expensive computer, when it has finished working out the sums required to produce a tape to tell one milling machine how to make one particular shape, can be set to work to calculate other tapes for the production of other shapes by a series of other machines that may be either in the same factory or in other factories that have sent in drawings.

The idea of mechanisation, of getting a steam-engine to do the mechanical work of a thousand men all gathered together in a factory rather than having each man do his own work separately in his own workshop by muscle power, was a general idea. It was, indeed, the idea behind the Industrial Revolution. Although it depended on the steam-engine working with coal as the basic source of the power, very many ancillary ideas later became woven into the fabric of industrialisation, eventually to reach its final flower with Mr Charlie Chaplin madly screwing up nuts at the travelling conveyor-belt in the apotheosis of all twentieth-century factories. In just this same way, although the new Industrial Revolution No. 2 is based on the general-purpose digital computer worked not by coal this time but by electronics, a number of supplementary ideas have been added, of which the most important is the linking device. The whole group of new notions has now given us 'automation'.

Up till the present there have been a number of industrial operations that have been done automatically. Tin cans in any well-conducted cannery can be seen being made up automatically from flat sheets and then automatically filled with automatically blanched (that is, scalded) peas, automatically sealed, automatically sterilised, labelled and packed into cartons. Things like milk bottles and electric lamp-bulbs can *only* be produced on an economic scale in very large factories in which most of the operations are automatic. The manufacture of motor-cars has perhaps represented the highest development and the last phase of Industrial Revolution No. 1.

The two major categories of operation in making a motor-car are machining and assembly. Although both of these have been highly mechanised, in each some element of human thinking has remained. The men working the drilling and milling machines have to think about putting the pieces in the right place before the machines are permitted to start the actual work. On the assembly line, the men and women have to think, even if by a minimal amount, about which screw to turn and which bolt to tighten. The beginnings of Industrial Revolution No. 2 are the great transfer machines that automatically move the metal pieces from station to station where a whole series of operations are performed. And in assembly we now have the computer watching over the components coming along the several diverse conveyor lines, so that a complete finished article—or at least a major section of one—can be put together without anyone having to think about it at all.

In industrial operations the margin between thinking and not thinking is a narrow one. This is why, if we accept that whereas the first Industrial Revolution was the mechanisation of muscle power and the second is the mechanisation of brain power, it is not altogether easy to prove that there has been a second industrial revolution at all. When the wise old man who has lovingly dug the garden, putting forty years of experience into every stroke of his spade, is displaced by a motor cultivator have we mechanised only muscle power? It is less easy still to know what we have mechanised when the skilled toffee boiler or Swiss-roll maker is displaced by a thermo-electric cut-out or an automatic travelling oven 150 yards long. But it is true to say that these people, however skilled and experienced they might be, were 'workers'. The originality of the electronic computer, and of the ancillary devices it has brought with it, is in its ability to mechanise some of the managerial, or 'white-collar', operations.

A computer with a long memory can deal very efficiently with office accounting. In certain European banks all the operations surrounding the cashing of a cheque have been mechanised by using a suitable computer. A slight modification is necessary in the client's customary habits. Instead of being issued with a cheque book, he has to cope with a uniform punch-card cheque instead. Even this minor inconvenience may be overcome if American investigators succeed in their present efforts to make 'original documents' capable of being scanned by automatic readers. Current reports are that British banks, although willing to introduce individual pieces of mechanical equipment, such as calculating machines and television sets for verifying signatures, are proposing to defer any attempt to introduce automation, and continue the present system, in which each of the several million cheques passing each day is copied six or seven times by a different person each time, for the somewhat bizarre reason, it is said, that they want to preserve the traditional banker-customer relationship.

A computer cannot 'think' in the sense that it can indulge in any form of original cerebration. It can, indeed, only do what its designer has arranged for it to carry out and no more. But the range of activities to which it can be adapted is large. For example, serious efforts have been made to design an electronic machine for translating languages from one tongue to another. The implications of this are somewhat remarkable.

The present international teleprinter code for transmitting individual letters by wire is a numerical one. Instead of using decimal numbers the binary scale is usually employed to give certain technical advantages but this makes no difference in principle. To construct a machine to translate from one language to another, it is not feasible to try to do it letter by letter. The words and syntax have to be broken up into semantic units. In many languages, particularly German, there are single words each of which includes within itself a number of separate pieces of meaning, or semantic units. On the other hand, there are often words that possess no meaning at all. The definite article in English is often 'vacuous', as the technicians put it. And in French 'ne . . . pas' share only one semantic unit between them. Be that as it may, some success has already been achieved in designing a memory for a computer comprising the necessary minimum of English semantic units. These can be stored in a series of rapidly revolving magnetic drums. A Russian text can be fed into the machine, either by being typed in on an electric typewriter or, if this is not rapid enough, by allowing a photo-electric system to scan the passage it is desired to translate. In the most elementary arrangement, the translation of the Russian into English was almost devoid of syntax or literary grace. But it seems now to be merely a matter of taking the necessary trouble and spending enough money on the machine to obtain a rendering as elegant as a passage of Macaulay.

An electronic computer can be set up to deal with any situation for which there are rules. For example, Professor Wiener of the Massachusetts Institute of Technology has worked out the requirement of a computer capable of dealing with every eventuality in the game of chess up to two moves ahead. The machine appears to any human opponent to play rather slowly but it is in fact playing over *every* eventuality in its 'head' before it announces its move. It can, in fact, on its own play up to a good first-class standard but it draws too often to be accounted a master. A more elaborate model can, however, be made to store away in its electronic memory every game it has ever played. Eventually, therefore, this machine will become a very good player indeed.

The ability to construct a machine capable of dealing with the contingencies of a game of chess opens up some remarkable possibilities. The rules of war are not quite so definite as those of chess but nevertheless 'logistics' is now recognised to be a systematic study. Mr Claude Shannon of the Bell Telephone Laboratories has suggested that an electronic computer might be usefully employed to evaluate a military situation and determine, just as in chess, the best move at any time in a campaign.

The last word, however, must be attributed to the logical mind of a Frenchman. Père Dubarle has pointed out that experienced politicians are well aware that the reactions of population groups to any particular political move are predictable and follow certain rules. These, again, may not be quite so regular as the rules of chess or the relations that link a word or phrase in Russian to its corresponding equivalent in English. Closer study of the behaviour of the electorate would, however, make the rules governing their behaviour sufficiently precise to allow an astute politician to base his policy on the advice of a suitably equipped electronic computer.

Perhaps these considerations may seem somewhat speculative in a discussion of the present state of the achievements of scientific thinking. If so, we can leave them aside, for the implications of what we can all see happening this moment before us are striking enough. The mathematical and scientific ideas that have led to the development of a general-purpose computer with the ancillary development in linking machines and 'feed-back' systems that correct their own errors, *combined with* the social ideas that recognise the justice of paying high wages, make it certain that automation will quickly and radically reduce the amount of time that men and women are required to spend at their paid employment. We already have industries in which the four-day week is accepted. Next will come, one cannot doubt, the three-day week. And there is no reason why this should not be turned into the six-month year. Or perhaps people may prefer to work the twenty-three-and-a-half-year lifetime and retire on full pay at forty-one. There is no reason why they should not and still draw their pensions at sixty-five as at present. Whatever they choose to do, there seems little doubt that the scientific thinking we have been talking about, whether we attribute it to a few original people like Charles Babbage or to the trend of philosophical materialism as a whole, is going to allow us for the first time in history to free ourselves from much of the burden of economic need. And when we do not *have* to work, then we shall come face to face with the more interesting question—what is the purpose of a civilised, scientific, twentieth-century man?

5

# INDUSTRIAL NUTRITION

ROBERT LOUIS STEVENSON in his parable of Dr Jekyll and
Mr Hyde illustrated man as a two-sided creature in whom the
good is opposed by the bad. We have already referred to another cause of lopsided human development, with scientific
philosophy applied only to material objects when it could
equally well be used to reach decisions on other topics as well.
But where we modern people show our cloven personalities
most strikingly is when we try to grasp the undeniable conclusions of science about food and nutrition while at the same
time prejudice, custom, folk-lore and all the dark motives of
illogic pull us away from what we do not want to understand.

How painful is the sight of the learned man, an ornament of
his College, a clerk in holy orders perhaps, who is—on what
evidence who can tell?—convinced that white bread is poison
and brown bread with flakes of bran in it the only way to
dietetic salvation. Then there are the otherwise intelligent
people who avoid potatoes for fear of getting fat, and those
who claim that the only nourishment resides in food fertilised
with animal ordure. Unscrupulous and cynical men disgrace the
name of science by preying on this weakness of human reason

46

so that excellently well-fed ladies shall spend money on un-
necessary vitamins and 'health' foods.

Every nation and every group within each nation is convinced that it alone knows what is good to eat. The paw-paws
and the fish sauce, or the roasted pig and rice, or the pie that
mother used to make—we know by divine inspiration that
they are 'the little of what you fancy' that 'does you good'—
even if the infant mortality is soaring, the teeth of most of
the middle-aged people in the community decayed and the
children afflicted with skin disease and pot-bellies. We also
know by the same process of unthink that horse flesh is disgusting and fermented beverage harmful to the indigenous
African population.

In view of this heavy pressure of emotion that bears upon
each one of us when the nature of our own food is considered,
the scientific achievement in elucidating the facts of nutrition
during the last fifty years or so becomes even more significant.
And the basic facts that we need to carry about with us as a
part of an ordinarily good education are these. All food, to
rank as such at all, must be capable of being digested, absorbed
into the circulation and there combusted for energy. The
amount of energy available from any article, be it cabbage,
bread, meat or fat, can be measured in unit calories; in like
manner, the bodily expenditure of energy, recorded in the
same units—or any other appropriate units—can be assessed.
Next, the useful constituents of all foodstuffs, whatever their
taste, whether we eat them for breakfast or on toothpicks at a
cocktail party, are, besides those employed solely as fuel, proteins, mineral salts or a group of complex chemical components
generally known as vitamins.

This information, in the considerable detail in which it is
now known, has led to remarkable achievements in public
health. The conquest of rickets—the 'English disease' of
history; the end of scurvy that once exterminated ships' crews
and military campaigns and brought about the failure of
Scott's expedition to the South Pole and the death of its leader;

the mastery of beri-beri, not long since endemic among the poorer peoples of Asia; the end of pellagra that scourged the southern United States: all these have come from applying the conclusions of logical scientific observations, experiment and thought.

Rather than try at this moment to review the whole field of nutritional science as it has affected particular diseases, most of which are strange to us today, or even to discuss its impact on the health and growth of children, I should like to consider in what way all this knowledge contributes to the happiness as well as the physical status of those men and women whom we now, in this Age of the Gospel of Paid Employment, describe as industrial workers.

The successes of scientific nutrition were achieved in a society where substantial numbers of people had too little to eat. In the nineteenth century, epidemics, bred in poverty and malnutrition, arose from failures in the social system. In the decade following the 1914–18 war, when millions of men were out of work in Great Britain, malnutrition, again arising from poverty, was a major public health problem. Ignorance was in part a cause of nutritional disease, rickets contracted in childhood remained as a handicap to men and women in their working life. Inadequate consumption of calcium and other defects of diet were to some degree contributory causes of the bad teeth so widely to be seen in the British industrial population. When too much carbohydrate was eaten this automatically implied too little protein and led to damaged growth and physique. Nevertheless, it remains unquestionably true that the single, most potent cause of malnutrition—is poverty. And today there is in Britain no *poverty* among industrial workers. Many of the customers of industrial canteens may consider themselves to be underpaid but they would, almost to a man, be insulted if they were described as poor.

But this is not to say that a knowledge of the principles of nutrition is not important to an industrial caterer, nor does it imply that industrial canteens cannot contribute in a major degree to the welfare of the people who use them. The key point, however, is that the significant contribution that 'industrial nutrition' makes in 1957 is to the *welfare* of people who work in factories rather than to their health. On some occasions there are contributions to be made to the physiological requirement for calories or protein, for mineral components or vitamins, but no one under Western conditions today ever sees the disease, hunger oedema, due to insufficient calories, or beri-beri due to inadequate supplies of vitamin $B_1$. Scurvy is a rare medical curiosity in industrialised countries and the only nutritional disease ever likely to be encountered is obesity!

In medieval and ancient times, the children of artisans were taught to work with their hands from the age of four or five years upwards and the apprenticeship system meant that by the time a boy had reached his teens he was already experienced in his craft. A few years later, as a young man, he was a master craftsman with all the satisfaction to be gained from acknowledged skill and creative ability. All this became changed in the nineteenth century with the invention of mechanical power and the rise of the industrial towns. The employment of children under shocking conditions in factories took the place of their use as assistants, often to their fathers, in a workshop that was in some instances an annexe to a dwelling house. Because of the bad conditions in factories of the Industrial Revolution many of these unfortunate little waifs never reached adult life. Those who did remained the slaves of the machines and were denied the opportunity of enjoying the satisfaction of becoming craftsmen.

It was pointed out in a recent article by Dr Leslie Banks, Professor of Human Ecology in the University of Cambridge, that to the workers of the early years of the last century conditions in Britain today would appear Utopian. Hours of work are now less than half, wages are high, health and welfare services are secure, housing is reasonably good, and there are more facilities for the use of leisure. Nevertheless, there is something missing. The satisfaction of doing creative work has been withdrawn. The secure feeling of belonging to a family group all engaged in a common endeavour, of co-operating with a master and his men in a clearly discerned purpose, no longer exists. The swing of the pendulum has carried those who work in industry into large and impersonal undertakings, their homes are often in dormitory areas remote from the life of any city or coherent community centre and much of their leisure is spent in watching football matches or the trivial shadows on a cinema or television screen, passively, receptively and without the enjoyment of creation with their own hands or minds.

Today we are just beginning to realise that people cannot for long do good work in industry if they are merely spending their time in a factory in order to be able to spend what remains of the week doing something that they *really* want to do all the time. Professor Banks quotes Benjamin Franklin as saying 'Dost thou love life? Then do not squander time, for that's the stuff life is made of.' Those who work *merely* to earn enough money to live while they are not at work are, in fact, wasting half their lives. The new thinking about industry, all the modern talk about incentives, is a re-appraisal of the genuine motives that keep a man active and content. And in this modern industrial environment, in which automatic equipment is gradually taking over both the heavy muscular work of the past and the tedious repetition jobs as well, the canteen ostensibly designed to ensure adequate nutrition has a new role to fill. Its purpose is not primarily to provide the physiological needs of work-people whose health and nutritional status require supplementation, although hungry people will still come to be served. But it is to be a place where part of a meaningful working day can be spent; where civilised men and women can meet; where it is reasonable to eat and be refreshed. In time, the canteen may even become a place where people can talk and think as well as where they eat. Just as in earlier days a master and his apprentices sat down together for their meals in the middle of a day spent in a common purpose, it is,

I suggest, not too far-fetched to suggest that the modern works canteen could reasonably—and scientifically—come to contribute in like manner to the welfare of the industrial workers of a modern factory.

This is not to say that the discoveries of nutrition are not of importance to a highly paid industrial worker. Of course, the fact that he is a 'worker' has very little to do with the matter, it is almost sufficient that he is a human being. For example, there are many devoted wives to be found who, even in this age of equality of the sexes—economic equality, that is, not physiological—are convinced that a man who steps into his car in the morning, spends the day sitting, either at his telephone or at the console of an automatic power press, and then drives home at five o'clock, needs more to eat than the rest of the family. Calorific requirements, that is the amount of food needed, depend on three minor factors: body size, age and what is known technically as basal metabolic rate—that is, whether one's character is lively, excitable and tense, or calm, phlegmatic and deliberate. But the major physiological criterion deciding whether one requires more or fewer calories is the amount of mechanical work done. Here the word 'work' is used in its scientific sense rather than in the ambiguous and emotional manner in which it is employed in common speech. Under this definition a lady running upstairs with a handkerchief for her demanding child is doing more work than the tradesman in the kitchen who is replacing the broken windowpane, since she is carrying 115 lb of woman up a height of 10 feet whereas he may merely be rubbing his thumb over the soft putty.

It is, of course, true that different types of work demand different amounts of energy. Out-of-door workers, like loggers or farm labourers (unless they are riding about on mechanically-propelled equipment), may expend up to 4,500 calories a day or more. Coal-miners appear to use up about 3,600 calories a day, but their needs depend on their actual jobs. These figures can be compared with the daily output of about 2,400 calories by sedentary men in offices or company board rooms and 2,000 calories on average by women who spend much of their days at typewriters or bridge tables.

But the justification for giving any special attention to the nutrition of *industrial* workers as a separate category is disappearing. More than twenty years ago now, in 1935 to be exact, it was pointed out at a meeting of the Institute of Civil Engineers in London that no sensible person ought ever to pay a man—or for that matter a woman—to do muscular work. Even at that time the cost of one horse-power of work produced by the muscles of a coal-miner varied between 10s. and 28s. 9d., whereas the same work could be produced by mechanical means for a penny. Nowadays, with the higher cost of human labour on the one hand and the parallel improvement in automatic processes and controlling systems in industry on the other, the use of human beings to develop muscle power is becoming less and less reasonable unless circumstances are quite remarkably unusual. And it is only physical muscular activity that has a direct call on increased calories from the diet.

I have said above that under modern Western conditions it is only under most exceptional circumstances that anyone would nowadays burn up muscle calories to produce industrial power. Some few thousand years ago Pharaoh used muscle power for building pyramids and not long after the 1939–45 war an article appeared in the *Economist* suggesting that muscle power could again be profitably exploited in this manner.

The suggestion was based on the calculation that the mechanical efficiency of a man producing work by means of a machine such as a bicycle is about 25 per cent. That is to say, he produces as work about one-quarter of the energy-value of the food consumed in doing the work. This is about the same as the efficiency of a railway locomotive. It was then further calculated that if there were a group of idle men or women—in refugee camps in Germany, or the Gaza Strip, or Torquay—they were capable of producing an economic return in the form of power for the investment of the supplementary calories they would need to eat over and above what they were eating anyway. A basic shortage in an industrial country is power. A high-standard country like the United States is able to supply more mechanical power for the assistance of each working individual than one like Portugal, where it is a commonplace to see a woman of sixty carrying on her head a load of fish up a hill. Coal has been a source of wealth to any country exporting it, at least within the last generation, which is, of course, merely a further reflection of the valuable nature of power. The ingenious suggestion of the *Economist* article was that 'cyclo-locomotives' be constructed, each capable of seating forty or more people whose combined thigh-muscle power would be sufficient to draw a train. By this means the coal otherwise required for the railway would become available as a valuable national export. Although the physiological and mechanical calculations involved in this proposal have not been seriously challenged, it is perhaps doubtful whether social considerations would allow the employment of even bored long-stay members of refugee settlements in this manner.

With the onset of the automatic age, one of the few increasing nutritional disabilities is obesity. There is a direct statistical relationship between obesity and early death, and consequently considerable scientific thought has been given to the problem of how to become more prosperous without getting fatter. The progress of knowledge in this field has in some small degree demonstrated to the sensitive scientific philosopher the danger of arrogance. Basically, the question of obesity is one of calorie balance. The calorific value of foodstuffs can be measured with some accuracy; the expenditure of calories in different types of bodily activity can also be measured; it therefore follows, in the style of Mr Micawber, that if a man does more work than his diet can support, he will become thinner from the need to combust his own tissues. On the contrary, if he eats more than he requires for his daily energy expenditure, he will get fatter. The non-scientific implication of this logic, be it accepted ever so little, is that fat people are greedy. And so we have had the unseemly spectacle of the self-satisfied lean man dining with a stout friend who is achieving prodigies of self-denial for which he can expect no praise or recognition. Recent observation of fact, supported first by inference and then by experiment, shows that the principle of calorie balance is indeed true, and that in most people an organ called the hypothalamus at the base of the brain enables them to maintain this balance. When the hypothalamus is deranged, appetite is no longer a measure of physiological need and one grows fat. There is no virtue in remaining, as most of us do, of normal girth throughout our adult life, it is a matter only of good fortune.

The principles of science are easy to understand, but to be a great scientist three things are necessary. The first is knowledge. That may be acquired by diligence. The second is intuition. This cannot be commanded. Poets call on the Muses to assist them. Not all scientists do. The third attribute for which a scientist must hope is negative; the ability to avoid the *non-sequitur* that is obvious to everyone else.

During the 1914–18 war Embden, a distinguished German physiologist, noted the recently discovered fact that phosphorus plays an essential part in the release of energy in muscle. From this he reasoned that it was self-evident that supplementary phosphorus must assist muscular performance. Consequently, he used his considerable authority to persuade the German authorities to provide a phosphate drink for large numbers of soldiers and workmen. He overlooked the fact that almost all normal diets provide ample phosphorus, so his efforts were wasted.

A similar lesson, it seems, constantly needs re-learning. Earnest dieticians of our own day have been known to press raw cabbages, salads, Graham bread, carrots and a variety of other commodities upon workmen without first seriously investigating whether their normal diet is defective. Multi-vitamin pills have been given to increase vigour, to ward off colds, to reduce absenteeism and to prevent accidents. On every occasion when trials have been planned with adequate control and on a statistically valid basis it has been found that under the ordinary conditions of British industrial life today no benefit has been obtained. That is to say when a man is obtaining adequate nutrition from ordinary foods he gets no supplementary advantages from eating vitamin pills.

Truth indeed lives at the bottom of a well. Remarkable things have been done with the methods and tools of science; nevertheless, it is still difficult for a scientist to be wise. For example, there are papers to be found in respectable parts of the scientific literature of the West that purport to show that the nutritional status and physiological efficiency of man, as a biological species, is improved if he eats a hot breakfast! Who among the elect at the United Nations will be first to lead the new crusade among the cold-breakfast and no-breakfast-eating infidels in the outer darkness of error?

An elaborate scientific experiment was reported in 1940 under the title of 'The Hawthorn Experiment'. A group of workers assembling telephones in a factory in the United States was studied in great detail. When they were given additional snacks and cups of tea their output of assembled telephones increased. But the number of telephones they put together became greater still when they were next given a short rest without any food; and it rose again when the lighting was improved, or when the ventilation was changed. In subsequent experiments all the changes previously made—the snacks, the fresh air, the light, the rest pauses—were one by one unmade but, to the surprise of the scientific observers, the manufacture of telephones got faster and faster. Finally, the conclusion was reached that the true factor stimulating the workers was not nutrition or physiology but the knowledge that they were important and of interest to someone.

We are living in the age of the scientific specialist. Every aspect of health is dealt with by a different expert. The oto-rhinolaryngologist copes with a man's ears, nose and throat, the psychologist with his mind and the cardiologist with his heart. The work's engineer is an expert on machinery and the ventilating consultant is an expert on draughts. The nutritionist may know all there is to know about calories and vitamins. And the first principle in feeding the people who work in the modern industrial world is to see that they have the nutrients they require for their age, sex, degree of activity and individual idiosyncrasies.

There is growing concern over the amount of food available in the world, particularly when the vast increases in population are taken into consideration. Technologists have studied this problem in great detail and the following chapter describes only one of the blind alleys which await the unwary in the pursuit of this elusive hare.

# 6

## SCUM

In July 1953, a book was published with the forbidding title of *Algal Culture*. On glancing through it, one might have thought that it was just one more technical monograph, of interest only to specialists in one of the restricted fields of modern science. It bore all the normal hallmarks of scientific respectability. Its pages were sprinkled here and there with mathematical formulae and diagrams and the flyleaf bore the imprint of the Carnegie Institution of Washington. But although the text was couched generally in a studiously even tone, there was in it an underlying element of excitement.

Ever since Malthus wrote his essay on population in 1785, we have had available the arithmetic needed to calculate how much food supply and population must deviate before starvation becomes a serious public-health problem. Some people take Malthus's warning more seriously than others. But most of us, whether we view the matter as one of urgency or not, have been struck at one time or another with the wastefulness of nature which, in order to produce a single ear of corn, a substantial proportion of which is itself uneatable, has to go to all the trouble of growing leaves, a long stalk and a whole paraphernalia of supporting and protective structures. Why is all this necessary, we may ask? The volume to which I have referred above summarises a large amount of modern scientific information about the cultivation of unicellular green crops. When these are grown it is not necessary to throw away the major part and only eat a specialised organ, such as the fruit, or the sap (as in sugar-cane), or a special leaf bud (as in the brussels sprout). There is a botanical family which produces only one cell: no leaves, stalks, flowers or grain—nothing to be thrown away—just itself. This basic prototype green thing can be eaten, it appears. In general the plants now intensively studied scientifically have been quite well known to the layman in connection with ducks, although completely ignored as a food for human beings. They are, indeed, algae—the green scum on ponds.

Human beings eat all sorts of things as food, animals of many different kinds, animal secretions such as milk, birds and their eggs, fish and *their* eggs (as caviar), crustacea, mollusca, in some countries insects, and in many countries insect secretions, notably honey. In the plant kingdom, very many botanical families even including certain varieties of seaweed contribute to the sustenance of man. But from whatever source it may come, human food, if it is to be defined scientifically as food at all, must be composed of constituents which can be used as fuel by a human body or which can be built into the structure of a man or in some way regulate his biological machinery. All of these constituents, the so-called nutrients, must previously have been elaborated by living cells. And the basic process by which these nutrients are elaborated is, of course, photosynthesis, when the green chemical in plants converts carbon dioxide gas from the atmosphere into plant substance. The energy for this process is produced by sunlight.

To revert to *Algal Culture*, the remarkable feature about the appearance of this dryly written technical book, edited by Dr John S. Burlew and produced by a hard-headed scientific body such as the Carnegie Institution of Washington, D.C., is that today in the age of confident scientific claims to understand almost everything, the subject with which it deals seems to possess a certain dream-like character. For example, Dr Burlew starts by describing an apparatus in which Chlorella, the type of alga best suited to domesticity, has already been grown. If this apparatus were expanded to cover an area of an acre, he calculates that 17½ tons of material could be produced in it in a year, and if it were then again expanded to the improbable extent of a million acres it could produce half of all the protein required to feed the present population of the world.

A further suggestion made by Dr Burlew is that we may be able to use Chlorella, not only for food, but to make our own coal without waiting for the passing of tedious geological epochs. Or, at least, it is seriously suggested that besides growing algae to eat it would be conceivable, provided the right kind of culture vessels and equipment were designed, to grow enough to burn as well.

Although the large-scale production of algae demands energy for pumping water and other necessary engineering activities and for drying the material grown, there is, if the Carnegie calculations are correct, more energy to be got back than is put in. And this book now solemnly suggests that an 'algal culture unit', as it is called, combined with a steam generating plant using the algae as fuel could one day be expected to provide us with our electric power. It is all worked out that by the year 2050, when all our coal, oil and fissionable materials may have been used up, we can get the energy we require if we devote one acre per head of the world's population, amounting to eleven million square miles in all, for the erection of power stations run on algae! This indeed is 'scientific' planning on the grand scale.

After this it is quite a contrast to read a chapter in the book contributed by a group of Dutch scientists working at the Agricultural University at Wageningen in Holland. In 1948, they grew their Chlorella in pint bottles, but by 1951 they had changed over to vessels with a surface area of one square yard.

In the bottles they achieved an efficiency of conversion of light energy into plant substance of 24 per cent, but on the larger scale they were only able to convert about 3 per cent of the energy in the sunlight falling on to the tank. Very honestly they pointed out that this was no better than the efficiency obtained by growing grass in a field. They concluded, paradoxically, that the efficiency of energy conversion would be greater if sunshine were not so bright.

British experiments carried out since 1949 are reported in this same book by Dr M. J. Geoghegan. Again, the work seems to have been done on a modest scale and the biggest vessel used was a tank 4 feet 6 inches high, 1 foot 6 inches long and 4 inches broad. All sorts of difficulties had to be overcome ranging from ways to prevent the algae from settling on the bottom to complicated tests to find out what mineral salts had to be added to fertilise them while growing. The food value of the final dried product was examined by feeding it to rats. Although it was only 65 per cent as nutritious a source of protein as dried skim milk it was 35 per cent *more* nutritious than groundnuts.

After considering the science of Holland and England, Dr Burlew turns to Japan and his book contains two chapters contributed by investigators at the Tokugawa Institute for Biological Research in Tokyo. There are photographs of the apparatus against a background of Japanese garden scenery. The Chlorella is shown growing in a concrete trench 45 feet long and passing through a tower 12 feet high where it is regenerated with carbon dioxide, the whole arrangement being controlled from a low building housing the pumps and filters. These chapters are set out with all the academic punctilio of Western science, chemical formulae, diagrams, footnotes and the use of the passive voice. But just occasionally a phrase or intonation discloses that this research has been done in Tokyo and not South Kensington. 'The cover of plastic sheeting', write Drs Mituya, Nyunoya and Tamiya, describing their outdoor trough, 'also caused some trouble. It was found to be resistant to heaps of snow, at least up to 30 cm. thickness, but was easily broken by such mechanical strains as those caused by dogs walking or running on it, as often occurred during our experiments. The inner surface of the sheeting was often covered with condensing water droplets, which appreciably reduce the available light intensity. Improvements are necessary to eliminate these shortcomings.'

The tenor of the chapter from the Hebrew University at Jerusalem brings us back again to the prevailing mood of earnestness. The great possibilities of trapping sunshine as food and energy for man without the necessity for waiting for the slow processes of nature have not yet been realised. Nevertheless, the Israel scientists started work in 1951 with the conscious idea in mind to grow algae to overcome their lack of arable land and of water to feed their thrusting population. The originality of the idea and its apparent scientific logic fit in well with their urgent needs and with the principal natural resources of their nation—energy, brains and above all sunlight. They calculate that a plant with an area of about two and a half square *miles* would provide 30,000 tons of material a year. But so far the algae have only been produced in a laboratory, although a pilot plant tank of nine square feet is planned. As one reads their chapter, however, in spite of the disparity between achievement and desire, the unreality of the whole business seems somehow less—it *ought* to be possible to grow algae like this. Theoretically it *can* be done: perhaps these people *will* do it. After all, it's not so long since penicillin was only produced in vessels the size of milk bottles.

In the long section of the book contributed by United States scientists working at Cambridge, Massachusetts, the growth of Chlorella begins to seem a matter-of-fact affair after all. The apparatus finally designed consisted of 500-foot lengths of flexible plastic tubing measuring 4 feet across. The liquid culture of Chlorella was pumped through this tubing round a flat roof. All the difficulties mentioned by others who had attempted the same task were encountered (with the exception of the Japanese dogs). Wind blew gravel on to the roof and made punctures in the plastic pipe; rotifers, that is microscopic animalcules with rotatory swimming organs, got in and ate up the algae; the temperature of the brew got too hot, or alternatively, too cold; one complete unit was built but refused to work at all. Throughout the chapter, however, as tables successively appear showing growth per day related to light intensity, or rate of flow and turbulence compared with the concentration of Chlorella cells per cubic centimetre, the impression strengthens that the technical problems can be made to resolve through diligence and perseverance. 'It is believed', write the authors, 'that although several problems remain to be solved commercial operation with tubes of this type is feasible.'

Needless to say, in this age of scientific feeding, a large number of laboratory analyses have been made of the nutritional composition of the dried algae produced by means of this arrangement of pipes. Besides the protein they contain, they have more vitamin A activity than carrots and are richly endowed with a series of B vitamins—from vitamin $B_1$ all the way to vitamin $B_{12}$. An interesting section of Dr Burlew's book reviews all the available references to the use of algae as human food. The seaweed, Irish moss, is a member of the algal family which has been eaten for a great many years. In Japan, other seaweeds are also considered to be delicacies. Microscopic algae, however, have apparently not been eaten before and the American investigators consequently set out to examine their taste with the usual systematic and unemotional thoroughness. They described it as 'foodlike' but with some unpleasantly strong 'notes'. A further scientifically defined attribute which they called the 'gag factor' was a tightening of the back of the throat and a lingering mildly unpleasant aftertaste. So it seems as if mealtimes in the year 2050 will take a little getting used to! Other experiments showed that when mixed to the extent of 15 per cent with what was described as 'chicken base' soup, the disagreeable strong 'notes' and the 'gag factor' were 'less evident'.

The algae produced experimentally at Cambridge, Massachusetts, in 1951 were not actually used as human food. But what is in many ways the most remarkable chapter in the whole book is the description of a scheme to produce algae specifically for human consumption. The feeling of unreality which the matter-of-fact scientific jargon from Cambridge, Massachusetts, only partly dispelled comes back with renewed strength as one reads further and further into this chapter.

It seems that in 1932, a certain Jorgen Jorgensen learnt of the demand in Scandinavia for vitamin A for addition to margarine, to replace the butter so largely imported from Denmark. During his travels in South America he had observed that in certain regions of Lake Maracaibo there occurred patches of *aguo espesa*, which means literally 'thick water'. When this water was scooped up with a calabash dipper and filtered 'through a couple of old felt hats' a material was obtained which was very rich in carotene, the yellow pigment which gives carrots their vitamin A activity. This material was algae. The following year, therefore, Jorgensen obtained a concession from the Venezuelan Government for the recovery of algae from the lake and in 1938 the National Congress of Venezuela ratified an exclusive twenty-year agreement for the industrial use of the phyto-plankton, as it was designated. Tax was to be paid only on the weight of material first harvested but not on any subsequent increase by cultivation.

After the agreement was ratified all the difficulties which might have been anticipated in floating so romantic a project arose. At first the whole idea was received with ridicule in Europe and the United States. A pharmaceutical manufacturer who had encouraged the idea in 1934 was sceptical by 1940 when practical support was needed. A major food firm expressed the view that the project was scientifically sound but would not take any commercial interest in it. And so it went on until in 1941 the Venezuelan Government, perplexed at the reluctance of foreign and domestic capitalists to invest in the new industry, cancelled the concession.

But Jorgensen was not defeated. This time he persuaded the Venezuelan Ministry of Health and Social Welfare to finance a scheme for preparing cultivated 'algal soup' as an addition to the diet of the leper colony at the Cabo Blanco Leprosarium.

The algae were cultured in two hundred large bowls of unglazed baked red clay each set on top of a cement pillar three feet high. The bowls were filled with three or four gallons of water to which was added the seed culture of algae, obtained either from a special tank or from 'local mudholes'. A little chemical fertiliser was put in as well. After from nine to fifteen days the algae were ready for harvesting. Early in the morning, before the scum floated up towards the light, most of the water was syphoned off and in this way about two and a half pints of thick 'soup' remaining was obtained. Certain bowls were kept for seed to be used later on and it was found that the best growth was obtained in these if the water which evaporated was replaced by ordinary soda water, but not fresh soda water. It was specifically stated that the best stimulant for algal reproduction was stale soda water.

From 1942 to 1946, leprous patients of all ages from eight to seventy received algal soup. It was boiled for twenty minutes and a little salt added to improve the flavour. Children were given three-quarters of a pint daily and adults about a pint. Owing to the fluctuations in their disease it was difficult to tell whether it did them any good but, as the authors report, 'no ill effects resulted from it'.

For a long period in the history of human thought men reached conclusions on the basis of many different kinds of philosophical considerations. It is only during the comparatively recent period of modern science that we have arrived at most of our material views on Nature on the basis of verifiable experimental observation. The method is simple. Let us once more repeat it. A series of facts is recorded, a hypothesis depending on these facts is drawn up, a speculative forecast based on the hypothesis is thought out, and an experiment designed to prove or disprove the hypothesis. The monograph under review is a case in point. The facts recorded in it are incontrovertible. Chlorella *does* make use of sunlight to convert carbon dioxide from the atmosphere into carbohydrate capable of being used as food by animals and man. The process *is* more economical than growing, say, wheat, most of which is inedible stalk or root or husk. Chlorella *does* also contain protein and vitamins. Since its growth does not require the use of soil it *ought to be* of value to a country like Israel which is short of land. For all these reasons there ought not to be anything strange about this 357-page volume of impeccable modern scientific reasoning. But there is.

Let us remember again the people who lived in the flying island of Laputa, always so wrapped in abstruse calculations that it was necessary for a servant to attend them at all times to prevent their tumbling over ordinary objects in their path. The description of Laputa was first published in 1726. Now in 1953, Dr Burlew in all earnestness writes of the artificial satellite of the future. 'A great deal of machinery will be needed in the space station', he says, 'to maintain a pseudo-terrestrial environment suitable for man. The addition of an algal culture unit for production of food for the inhabitants would not seem to increase in very large proportion the complexity of the structure.' Besides which it would, in his opinion, avoid the necessity for expensive journeys down to earth.

Algal culture is in many ways an attractive idea, and from what I have said of the great compilation published by the Carnegie Institution of Washington its study can be seen to engender enthusiasm among those working on it. It is, however, only one phase of a general scientific problem: how to obtain supplementary sources of food in addition to the articles of diet to which we are already accustomed. The universal raw material from which all foods is derived is sunlight. It is, therefore, reasonable to base a scientific assessment of the enthusiastic advocacy for Chlorella upon the degree of efficiency with which it transforms sunlight into food. N. W. Pirie, working in the oldest scientific research station for agriculture in the world at Rothamsted, has reviewed the matter and his calculations come as a rather cold douche after the exciting writings of Dr Burlew and some of his colleagues.

From such evidence as has been collected it seems that algae are no more efficient than the higher plants to which we are accustomed. The arrangements of shallow warmed tanks and plastic pipes and the occasional pumped supplies of carbon dioxide gas are every bit as expensive to run as the more conventional greenhouse. And in addition to the technical complications involved in most of the suggested methods of culturing algae, there is a danger of infection by micro-organisms. Although normal crop plants do suffer from diseases, two thousand million years of the catch-as-catch-can of evolution has rendered them remarkably resistant to most of the microbes floating about in the atmosphere or native in the soil.

There is only one point which algae might be expected to score: there is nothing to waste—if you eat it. There is no question of stripping off the leaves and eating only the grain on the cob (as with maize); or cutting off the leaves and eating the bulbous root (as with turnips); or perhaps extracting only the sugar from the root (as with sugar beet). Faced with the large amount of waste in our normal foods and the disadvantages of trying to produce algae, which even after they were produced might contain so high a concentration of 'gag factor' that they were practically unusable, Pirie has suggested two quite different, logical, and eminently scientific lines of investigation.

The first objective is to use sunlight more efficiently. For altogether too long the people of Britain have wasted their exiguous supply of sunlight. About half of the total annual supply of British sunlight is received by Midsummer Day. Yet scarcely any of it is used by many highly productive crops such as potatoes, because the air is too cold. Little photosynthesis is achieved by grasses during the first half of the year because the ground is too cold. Later in the year, sunshine that might be working at photosynthesis is again wasted, this time because farmers are waiting for grains to ripen and during this time little new food is created. In addition, the most efficient plant for catching and using sunlight for food manufacture would be one with its leaves growing all the way along a succulent stem, ensuring that little light reached the ground, where obviously it would be wasted.

There is no reason why more efficient plants should not be found. The present plants we use as food were selected by primitive man in a very haphazard manner. Of the half-million or so known green plants, only a few hundred are used on any significant scale and a number of these we enjoy vicariously by feeding them first to animals. But many of the others grow luxuriantly, and if we call them weeds today that is only because we have not yet made use of them.

The second line of profitable research would be to use the active protein-rich plant organ, namely the leaf, as a source of human food, rather than the miscellany of roots, grains, flowers and juices that are today so wastefully consumed. It is not suggested that, like Nebuchadnezzar, we should eat grass or similar whole leaves. They are altogether too fibrous for human stomachs. But then so are whole oats or wheat. Already, considerable study has been devoted to technical methods for extracting palatable protein from leaf. The standard three-roll sugar-cane mill was the result of five hundred years of mechanical trial and error, and the screw oil-expeller is also a traditional machine. Both these machines can be used to extract leaf protein but they work inefficiently for this purpose. An earlier instrument, but one designed for a similar use, has given more promising results. This is the woad presser.

This line of scientific thinking leads us to a rather different conclusion than that of the algae enthusiasts. Increased efficiency in using light to create food is to be achieved by using the strongest growing, leafiest plant. This may be what we now consider as a weed. The leaf of a plant is analogous to the liver of an animal. In it takes place the synthesis of whatever nutrients may later be sent to the roots or the fruits or the seed. So rather than waiting for the transfer to take place and thereby having to put up with a period of delay during which the conversion of soluble substances to fibre takes place, or maturity and ripening is carried out for the benefit of the plant rather than the advantage of man (when the fields of green corn turn golden, photosynthesis virtually comes to a standstill), the milling of edible substances will be done at the leaf stage. The exact method of milling has yet to be invented as an economic process but, with the example of woad manufacture before him, the modern scientist ought not to take long.

In a work entitled *Microcosmographia Academica* published in Cambridge in 1908, F. M. Cornford wrote: 'Nothing should ever be done for the first time.' It is easy to invoke the same attitude to projects for the direct use of leaf protein. The industrial production of leaf protein on a substantial scale as human food has not yet been achieved and nor has culture of the stalkless, huskless, pipless and rootless algae. But the economic advantages of at least the former as a way of increasing the yield of food have been worked out. Malthus may even now be proved to have been wrong for not having taken account of the fact that before they reach starvation point growing populations might develop scientific foresight.

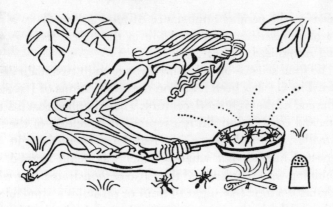

# 7

# EATING INSECTS AND OTHER
# HABITS

THIS is a scientific age. Science, however, develops unevenly at its different points. Just now it is atomic physics which is driving forward. In a little while this drive will slow and stop, and, perhaps, a period of consolidation will take place.

In the course of the last two chapters, I have been discussing certain aspects of food science. In this aspect of scientific thought as a whole there is some reason to believe that a pause for thought and reflection is occurring just now to allow, perhaps, for the new biochemical knowledge of what is going on in the animal machine to be related to the more mundane problems of how to advise people to choose proper meals. During the 1920's and 1930's the mechanics of nutrition were being worked out. First came the turn of calories and proteins and then came the era of vitamins which, indeed, is not yet over. For example, the current day-to-day discoveries of the scientific periodical literature are concerned with the subdivisions of vitamin $B_{12}$. But important though the facts of nutritional science are for keeping human groups in a state of health and efficiency, the parallel importance of food and meals as a part of a harmonious and civilised life in the fullest sense is also being recognised.

The food science of today has grown up in two main directions. The first has been based on the observations of Lavoisier at the end of the eighteenth century. These implied that fire and flame and combustion did not represent the release of the soul of matter, the phlogiston, as had long been thought but suggested instead that whatever fuel was being burned was combining with oxygen; and they also demonstrated that when such fuel is a food like sugar or flour or oil and is assimilable by the human body, it gives up in that human body the identical amount of heat and combines in that human body with the identical amount of oxygen as it does when burned outside the body. This conception was the beginning of the mechanistic tradition of nutrition which holds sway today, a tradition which is correct so far as it goes and has been enormously useful. The engineer in charge of a power station knows the calorific value of his fuel and can calculate the amount of electricity his machinery will generate from it. Similarly, a Ministry of Food knows the calorific value of its stocks of whale-meat, wheat and sugar and can calculate how much physical effort can be developed by a known population eating these supplies. The idea is not new. Indeed the philosophers of classical times discussed the paradox of the rich man whose needs for bodily labour were slight but whose table was amply covered with varied dishes, while the poor man who had to work all day possessed insufficient to assuage his hunger. But the precision and detail of the modern nutritional science is new and it is this command of detailed knowledge which has captured the imagination of the scientist of today, even to the extent of sometimes blinding him to larger issues.

The details of modern science are infinitely numerous but the capacity of the modern scientist's mind is not infinitely large. Thus it has happened that the experts on nutrition have on occasion been so fully occupied with the details of nutrition that they have had no time to attend to the doings of the food technologists.

Food technology is the second main development in food science. It ranges all the way from the applied genetics of the husbandman, who breeds a specially small sheep possessing a conveniently small leg to provide an appropriate joint for a modern small family, to include the canning expert who can convert a nondescript, bony, small fish of ambiguous genetical origin into a sardine possessing an agreeable flavour unknown to Nature. Scientific food technologists have also marched on to the triumphs of 'full fruit standard' jam, 'Household' dried milk, and the 'Spam' and 'deep-frozen' peas of modern civilised life.

At one time the nutritional scientist was ignorant of the doings of the technological food scientist and, when recognising his existence at all, was contemptuous of him. For example, considerable scientific effort was expended by the technologist in producing a 'marbled' joint of first quality beef while, at the same time, the standard text-book of nutrition calculated that the housewife's 'calorific penny' was far better spent on suet and mince than on the prime joint. A further example of the curious intellectual effects resulting from an excessive pre-occupation with the details of nutritional science is the way in which cooking is treated in most scientific treatises on nutrition. The losses of vitamin C and of vitamin $B_1$ are always fully discussed in detail and such topics as the 'denaturation' of protein and the leaching away of mineral salts take a prominent place. It might be supposed from all this that the effects of cooking are deplorable. And this conclusion was reached by the more enthusiastic protagonists of scientific eating, who adopted diets of raw carrots and frumenty. Perhaps the pause for thought and reflection to which I have referred now allows it to be respectable to discuss in scientific circles the *beneficial* effects of cooking as well as its allegedly harmful ones.

The 1939–45 war gave the nutritionist the opportunity of

testing his theories in practice. These, based on a mass of observation and experience collected over a period of one hundred and fifty years, were found to be sound but inadequate. That is to say, although man's nutritional well-being can be supported on a basis of calories, proteins, fats, minerals and vitamins, he does not live on these things alone. The life of the whole man includes matters dealt with by the anthropologist, the psychologist, the economist, the aesthete and the philosopher as well as by the nutritionist and the physiologist. And within the realm of nutritional science, other factors than nutrition must be considered. There is little food value in pickles but demand for them is insistent in every war in which Great Britain is involved. In fact, if one can believe the highly experienced catering officers in the War Office, British armies cannot fight without them.

Thus it has come about that science has begun to take an interest in the acceptability of foods as well as their chemical composition. Their nutritional value is important but such importance ceases if people refuse to eat them. Some consideration is now being given to new sources of food, such as food yeast made from sawdust or, as we have already seen, to protein derived from grass. And a few, a very few, glances are being spared for foodstuffs eaten by other races outside the orthodox circle of Western civilisation. Of these classes of potential edible commodities, one of the most interesting is the insects.

Man uses as food most of the important families of living creatures on this globe. Mammals of all sorts are readily consumed, vertebrate fishes, and invertebrates such as the octopus and the oyster. But civilised man has in recent years neglected insects. This is peculiar in view of the currency of the biblical cliché synonymous with plenty, 'flowing with milk and honey', in which bracketed together are the secretions of a mammal and of an insect.

Recently the scientific neglect of the insect species as food has been remedied by the publication of a scholarly book entitled *Insects as Human Food*, written in English by F. S.

72

Bodenheimer, the Professor of Zoology at the Hebrew University in Jerusalem, and published by Dr W. Junk at The Hague. As a general rule, dieticians and nutritional scientists restrict their reading to a fairly narrow range of text-books and to the periodical scientific literature in which are published the reports of various researches. These tend to deal with such topics as the losses of vitamin C occurring during the steaming of cabbages in industrial canteens or, alternatively, with the incidence of follicular keratosis (which can loosely be interpreted as goosepimples) among the middle age-groups at a university housing development site in the United States. Thus the appearance of Professor Bodenheimer's book was calculated to broaden the minds and at the same time develop the humility of professional nutritionists if they could be persuaded to read it.

An increase in humility is an essential feature of the period of consolidation and thought to which I have previously referred. Not long ago a dietary survey was made among the Otomi Indians in the Mezquital Valley in Mexico. The investigators were horrified to discover that these people ate none of the foods familiar to dieticians; neither spinach, brown bread, orange juice, carrots nor cod-liver oil appeared on their menu. Later it was discovered, however, that the mixture of pigweed, sow-thistles, cactus fruit and intoxicating pulque made from the juice of the century plant and the other ingredients of which their diet was composed possessed a higher nutritional content than the diet of a group of United States town-dwellers surveyed at the same time. Professor Bodenheimer now points out that the puzzling results obtained by a number of physiologists who have studied the diets of tropical races and found them to be apparently deficient in animal protein and fats, although at the same time the people were fit and obviously well fed, may well be explained by the fact that these people were accustomed to termites, caterpillars, locusts and other insects in substantial quantities as well as more conventional articles of diet. Either insects were not included in the questionnaires used by the Western scientists or their consumption was ignored. Yet Professor Bodenheimer's book very clearly shows that, where no preconceived prejudice exists, men show no aversion to entomophagy. We ourselves consume both milk and the cow that gives it, can we therefore object in principle to eating bees as well as honey?

John the Baptist lived in the desert on insects: locusts and wild honey. Professor Bodenheimer points out that many people eat locusts. In the palace of the great King Asurbanipal near Nineveh in the eighth century B.C. locusts arranged on sticks, as we today might eat prawns or chipolata sausages, were served at the royal banquets. Today in Tanganyika locusts are still widely eaten. With wings and hindlegs removed they are roasted or fried in butter, when their flavour is reminiscent of shrimps. Flying locusts and hoppers are dried in the sun and eaten as a flavouring for porridge. To the west and south of Lake Victoria, green grasshoppers are eaten in large numbers either fresh or dried and a giant cricket is dug out of the ground, roasted and eaten as a relish. Professor Bodenheimer writes that many observers have found that in the Sudan and elsewhere in Africa when the locusts arrive the people eat them in such quantities that they grow fat within a few days. Dr Livingstone reported that roasted locusts possessed a vegetable flavour, and considered that, on the whole, he preferred them to shrimps. M. le Vaillant, writing of South Africa in 1782, described the joy of the local inhabitants at the appearance of locusts. Their flavour, he said, was like that of the yolk of a boiled egg. Another French writer, Daguin, compared the taste of locusts to that of caviar!

M. Decary, in two recent papers, one published in 1937 and one in 1950, describes how locusts are caught in Madagascar where, together with other grasshoppers, they form an important local food. The French railway authorities apply the same transport charges to dried locusts as they do to game and fish. Decary compares their flavour to that of hazel nuts. Father Camboue in 1886 told how Queen Ranavalona II employed a band of women whose duties were to scour the fields for locusts so that the royal table at Tananariva might always be well supplied.

It seems that locusts, with or without wild honey, may be made into an attractive and nourishing dish. A traveller in North Africa declared that locust soup reminded him of nothing so much as crayfish bisque and said that he would gladly see it on his table every day. He prepared the soup by boiling the locusts briskly, having previously seasoned them with salt, pepper and grated nutmeg. When cold, they were pounded with bread fried brown or with a purée of rice. They were then replaced in the saucepan and thickened to a broth on the stove but not allowed to boil. Finally, the broth was strained and a few croutons added. A further recommendation for the use of locusts as an article of diet is that they are as acceptable and nourishing for camels as they are for men.

Termites are also widely eaten in the countries in which they are found. They are insects which organise themselves in elaborate colonies and which often build 'ant-hills' of considerable size. In May one can find at the market at Leopold-ville in the Belgian Congo baskets full of fried termites which, so Professor Bodenheimer tells us, are sold for fifty-four centimes a small handful. They are also used as a source of oil, which is stated to be of good quality and excellent for frying. He quotes Sir S. W. Baker who, writing in 1881, reported that in Central Africa termites fried in butter are considered a very delicate meal. He himself found that they had a 'light flavour of burned plums'. At certain seasons of the year the winged termites swarm. Great excitement ensues among the local inhabitants and all sorts of methods are used to catch them. A gentleman called Henry Smeathman described what happens in the *Philosophical Transactions of the Royal Society* in 1781. In the part of Africa where he was the people dried the insects in iron pots over a gentle fire, stirring them about as is usually done when roasting coffee. 'In that state', he wrote, 'without sauce or any other addition, they serve them as delicious food. And they put them into their mouths as we do comfits. I have eaten them dressed this way several times, and think them both delicate, nourishing and wholesome; they are something sweeter but not so fat and cloying as the maggot of the *Rynchophorus palmarum*, which is served up at all the luxurious tables of West India.'

A species of ant which has its attractions as human food is the so-called 'sugar ant' of Central Australia. These ants select from among the workers of the colony certain individuals whom they proceed to stuff with food until their abdomens swell to the size of marbles. 'The ant in this condition', says Professor Bodenheimer, 'is naturally unable to move from the spot. It appears that the inflated ants in this extraordinary way provide for the needs of the colony during the barren season of the year, acting as living barrels which can be tapped as required.' The honey with which the creatures are filled originates from sweet exudations of certain plant galls and from the honey-dew of other insects. The local Australians eagerly consume these ants by gripping them by the head, placing the inflated abdomen between their lips and squeezing the contents into their mouths. As regards taste, the first reaction the palate receives is a distinct prick of the formic acid with which the ant hopes to protect itself. But this is both slight and momentary; and the instant the membrane bursts, it is followed by a delicious and rich flavour of pure honey. A similar ant is also found and eaten in Mexico.

Another insect delicacy of which the Western table has been too long deprived is the palmworm. As with so many dishes, it is to a Frenchman that we owe one of the earliest descriptions, for Père Labat, who visited the West Indies at the beginning of the eighteenth century, appears to have been the first European to try it. This insect lives in the heart of palm-trees and is obtained when they are felled. The palmworm, so he reports, is as thick as a finger and about two inches long. 'It may be compared', he says, 'to a lump of fat from a capon wrapped in a very tender and transparent pellicle. They are placed in a row on a piece of wood and turned over a fire. When they begin to get hot, they are covered with breadcrumbs, pepper and muscat. They may also be boiled, when they are served with a few drops of lemon or orange juice. They are good to eat and very delicate.' A modern French author, M. Ghesquière, writing in 1947, says that the common palmworm of the Dutch East Indies is recognised as a most fortifying, easily digested food which is given for preference to weak and consumptive persons. Malayans in Europe often order them to be sent to their home. In Madagascar, the palmworm is consumed raw or fried. In the Belgian Congo it is greatly prized. The collectors search for them by putting their ear to the trunks of the palm-trees. An experienced operator can recognise the right moment for cutting down the tree and obtaining the larvae in the best condition for eating by the noise the insects make in nibbling at the fibres of the wood. Throughout the markets of Africa the plump larvae may be found either alive or fried in oil.

But insects are not only caught wild as food. They are also farmed as domestic animals. In Mexico, there is a variety of waterbug which is known locally as *ahuatle* or *bledo del agua*. These small insects provide food for man by the prodigious quantity of their eggs, which are collected as if they were a regular crop. A flour is made from them and used in baking cakes, which are variously described as 'of a pronounced fishy taste and slightly acid'; 'flavoured like fish roe'; and 'a delicacy'. The bugs abound in fresh-water lakes. Collectors place a number of bundles of a certain species of rush in the water. The bugs lay their eggs on the rushes, which are then taken out of the lake and beaten on great sheets of cloth to detach the myriads of eggs with which they are covered. These are then cleaned, sifted and put into baskets, while the rushes are replaced in the water to gather another crop.

There is an insect which, like the sheep, has been for many centuries farmed both for the textile fibre it supplies and for the meat as well; this is the silkworm. In the process of reeling the silk, the cocoons containing the pupae are dropped into very hot water and the reeling girls thus have a plentiful supply of freshly cooked food before them all day long. 'One gets', quotes Professor Bodenheimer, 'the pleasant odour of food being cooked, when passing through a reeling factory.'

It is clearly apparent from this review that in different parts of the world insects of all kinds are used as human food and are found to be edible and palatable. Professor Bodenheimer passes indefatigably through one country after another listing ants, beetles, butterflies, moths, dragon-flies, caterpillars and spiders, each of which possesses its individual dietetic excellence. Besides the insects which are themselves eaten, there are the bees and sugar-ants which are also prized for the honey they produce, and the aphids. He quotes voluminous evidence to show that aphids supplied timely manna for the Children of Israel and continue to do so for the people who live within the limits reported in the Bible, namely Elim, now called Wadi Gharandel, and Rephidim, which is today the oasis of Teiran.

Finally, as is inevitable in the mid-twentieth century, Professor Bodenheimer quotes his scientific authorities who have analysed insects; L. Tihon, who in 1946 determined the dry matter, ash, fat and nitrogen content of termites, and proved that 100 grams of fried termites supplied 561 calories; Japanese authorities, who established the protein, carbohydrate and phosphorus content of silkworm pupae; and the numerous authorities who have listed the chemical composition of locusts and grasshoppers of different varieties.

But it is not for this type of information, valuable though it may be, that the thoughtful nutritionist will thank Professor Bodenheimer most. It is probably from the reference to the rare book by Mr V. M. Holt, published in London in 1885 and now only available in the University Library at Oxford, that the philosophical reader will obtain greatest stimulus. 'Cheese-mites', says Holt, 'are freely eaten by many persons as part of the cheese.' In the same way cabbage worms are only 'part of the cabbage'. And then he continues by describing how delicious are grasshoppers, cockchafers and wasp grubs. Finally, he gives two menus for the gentleman's dining table, of which this is one:

Snail soup
Fried soles with woodlouse sauce
Curried cockchafers
Fricassée of chicken with chrysalids
Boiled neck of mutton with wireworm sauce
Duckling with green peas
Cauliflowers garnished with caterpillars
Moths on toast.

Brillat-Savarin says, 'Anyone inventing a new dish does more for the happiness of his fellow men than all the philosophers, writers, scientists and politicians together.' If sardines were as expensive as oysters, the scientists whose skill and knowledge enable them to be prepared and preserved and canned to bring a novel flavour and nutritional value as well into the world would have been acclaimed as highly as the discoverer of a new vitamin. Perhaps the learning now given to the world by Professor Bodenheimer will open a new door through which science will contribute to the happiness as well as to the nutrition of mankind.

But here once more we find the possibility of a clash between the philosophy of scientific materialism and other philosophies of life in which aesthetics, reverence for tradition, even religion itself, enter as well. The scientific literature has a lot to say about the biochemical powers of selection possessed by all sorts of animals including man himself. There was a famous experiment in which a group of rats were presented with a long row of pots and tubes containing materials they could never possibly have encountered before in their normal wild life. These receptacles contained purified carbohydrates, fats, proteins, and solutions of potassium chloride, calcium lactate, sodium phosphate, choline chloride and many more. Isolated vitamins of eight or more sorts were also provided. Ungrateful populations in receipt of scientifically balanced rations sent by benevolent but conscientious welfare organizations have been known to cry: 'Give us food, not calories.' The situation facing the rats was the extreme case of their being given nutrients rather than food. Yet the results of the experiment were remarkable. The rats, without the benefit of science or education, chose for themselves what their investigators could only describe as a perfect diet according to the most up-to-date nutritional knowledge.

In a further experiment, another group of rats were compelled to choose from the only three beverages available to them to supply their needs for calories. These were a sugar solution, a solution of alcohol, and plain water. The two former can supply energy to a needy rat, the third cannot. When the experiment started, the rats obtained the bulk of their requirements from sugar and drank only a judicious proportion of alcohol. The investigator responsible for the trial then began surreptitiously to substitute a solution of saccharine, that possesses no food value at all, in place of the sugar. The animals responded by increasing the amount of alcohol they drank in almost the exact proportion needed to give them back the calories they had lost by the reduction in their sugar ration.

This type of experiment upon which the theory of the biochemical power of selection depends has been extended to babies. There is a historical anecdote that Charles II had the notion of sending two new-born babies in the care of a dumb nurse to live on a desert island. The object of the expedition was to discover whether or not the infants as they grew up would, as was traditionally supposed, start to converse with each other in Hebrew. Although this fascinating experiment has, so far as I am aware, never been carried out, a not entirely dissimilar one has been done with diet. Enterprising United

States investigators presented each of a group of infants with a number of saucers. These contained boiled egg, butter, sugar, chopped meat, greens, carrots, orange, milk, porridge, potato and a whole list of other single items. The infants were allowed free rein to stuff themselves with banana or jam or fish or cheese just as the spirit moved them. Although it was found that certain of the babies tended to 'go on a splurge' for a time and concentrate single-mindedly on one particular food, in general, the infants like the rats before them selected a nutritionally satisfactory diet. Furthermore, as a reward for the courage of the scientific investigators no harm came to any of the babies.

This kind of nutrition is, however, one side only of the philosophical picture. Powers of biochemical selection no doubt tell us to eat more protein or cut down our consumption of vitamins but they do not give us any information about why we consider horse-meat disgusting—that is, if we do. And Professor Bodenheimer's monograph on insect eating has not been followed by any pronounced change in dietary habits.

The experiments with rats carried out at the Johns Hopkins University School of Medicine, that I have just described, need to be done with great precaution. Rats, like men, are subject to what the psychologists call 'habituation'. For example, they get used to eating out of a pot placed in a special position in their cage and will refuse more nutritious food if it is put in an unfamiliar place. We ourselves are far more affected by 'habituation' than rats or dogs. We tend to get illogical views about the 'appropriateness' of articles of diet. An extreme case in Britain is that when oranges are used to make jam we will only eat it at breakfast. Although there is little difference in nutritional values, we consider sour milk nasty but cream cheese nice; putrid chicken bad but putrid pheasant good. A statistically designed trial of two chocolates of identical taste and consistency, one white and the other brown, showed that when people judged them blindfold they rated them equal. But when they could see the chocolate, the taste of the white one was described as 'fatty' or 'tallowy' and it was classed as generally inferior.

Science can provide precise information about nutritional requirements and their effect on physiological processes, but it is less sure in deciding between good food and bad food.

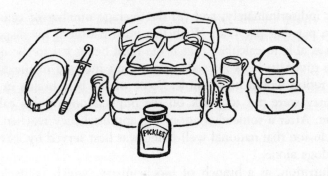

# 8

# BREAD AND SCIENCES

It was Monsieur Jourdain, in Molière's *Le Bourgeois Gentilhomme*, who suddenly discovered towards the end of his career that he had been talking prose all his life. A similar discovery has recently been made by the scientific nutritionists of today, that in spite of the essential need for calories, protein and vitamins, we have been eating food all the time—even in periods of disaster and shortage.

It is universally accepted that the scientific principles of nutrition enabled the people who administered the food supplies in Britain during the 1939–45 war to provide a remarkably sound diet even during a period of great scarcity. It is less well known that this was due, at least in part, to a recognition that in order to be nourished one must eat, but that in order to *want* to eat one must enjoy at least some measure of contentment.

There was, for example, the remarkable incident of the dogs. At one time a keen young Scientific Officer suddenly got the idea that it was very wasteful of food, in a country popularly considered to be fighting with its back to the wall, to support so many pet dogs. This young scientist caused a survey to be made in order to find out (*a*) how many dogs there were altogether, (*b*) what was the average weight per dog—lumping together, for the purposes of calculation, big dogs and little ones indiscriminately, and (c) the average number of calories eaten per dog per year. With this information at his disposal he was able to calculate that if the food being fed to the dogs were given to hens instead a significant increase in the basic egg ration would be possible. Some of the best brains in the country were put to work on the implications of this calculation. After a somewhat agonising appraisal they reached the conclusion that national well-being was best served by leaving the dogs alone.

Nutrition, as a branch of biochemistry, which is itself an offshoot of physiology, can be described as an exact science. That is to say, the necessary fuel for the efficient functioning of the human body can be exactly worked out provided that the body is that of an unconscious patient or, that mathematical abstraction, a statistically significant sample of an average population.

Nutritional principles hold good for an individual, just as the moral law or the Highway Code holds good, but the individual may not choose to comply. Even under conditions of impending disaster, the choice of what to eat may be influenced in a remarkable way by considerations other than those of nutritional orthodoxy.

In 1945, I had some responsibility for advising the military authorities on the feeding of the city of Vienna. My French, American and Russian colleagues and I sat round a table and, after reviewing the supplies available to us, worked out a diet guaranteed to supply the population with all the nutritional needs. There was no meat, but we issued beans instead to an amount calculated to provide the exact protein equivalent. But there and then in the face of disaster, the inhabitants of the city objected to the beans. 'Why,' they asked, 'whenever there is a war—and at no other time—do we get beans?'

There seems little doubt that our attitude to disaster is changing. Joseph, when he was appointed Minister of Food to Pharaoh, established in Egypt a system of bulk buying for a single commodity only—corn. In 1938, when Sir Henry French was set the task of laying in stores in Great Britain, he concentrated on three commodities, wheat, sugar and whale oil. And yet, when war came, the population would not be appeased by these simple staples. The plan for vegetables to supply necessary vitamins, potatoes, and cabbage for vitamin C, and carrots for vitamin A, had to be extended to include onions and gherkins for the manufacture of pickles (of negligible nutritional value), without which the armed forces could not undertake to face a seige.

But this is looking back. What of the present?

Atomic or hydrogen bomb attack, says an official publication, might mean that in a 'fall-out zone' a family might be required to stay under cover for as long as a week. Such living might mean isolation as complete as that of 'the lonely pioneer clearing', to quote the official phrase. There would be no electricity, contaminated water systems, crippled communications, and radiation danger beyond the doorstep. To meet such conditions, the United States Federal Civil Defence Administration is recommending that 'homemakers' shall now lay in what is called 'a seven-day emergency pantry'. The suggested list of items with which the modern suburban family is advised to provide itself to face the ultimate disaster of up-to-date, full-scale atomic war is a remarkable illustration of the current attitude towards disaster.

The first part of the list comprises canned juice, fruits and vegetables. Altogether, seventeen items are recommended: orange juice, grapefruit juice, tomato juice; grapefruit sections, peaches, pears, pineapple, plums, cherries, tomatoes, peas, beans and asparagus! Next, the castaways marooned in the radio-active solitude must have soup—tomato, mushroom, bean, vegetable and cream of chicken. The British observer will be gratified to see, heading the list of meats, corned beef, that trusted standby for emergency. But it is, of course, not alone. The American survivor can also fall back on beef stew, luncheon meat, tuna, chicken, canned ham or baked beans. And for spice and variety, pickles, catsup or chili sauce, mayonnaise, molasses, cookies and spaghetti with tomato sauce have not been forgotten. The list of beverages is also of interest. Besides dried milk, powdered tea and coffee, and chocolate syrup, canned cream is also to be stored away. For the staff of life, only canned date-and-nut bread, crackers and packaged cereals are recommended. And finally, bringing up the rear of the column of 'miscellaneous items' is the first essential for survival in a scientific world, a can opener.

When food is so scarce that there really *is* too little to eat, and when the shortage is so prolonged that the state of affairs is that of famine, people will eat almost anything. But at levels of deprivation only just removed from famine the innate complexity and irrationality of human behaviour—particularly on matters of eating and drinking—quickly become apparent.

People cast away in lifeboats are, perhaps understandably, prone to pessimism. Nevertheless, it is in some ways a strange thing that, in this age of high technical efficiency, of radio, and aircraft, and rapid movement about the globe, they are as pessimistic as they are. After all, this is a historical period when it is the general rule that we are surrounded by social organisations designed to help and protect each other. Yet in this environment, people in ships' lifeboats tend to behave as if no one were *ever* likely to come to their rescue. The bitter paradox is often seen after the loss of a ship, when men are rescued from boats suffering from acute lack of water and yet with most of the boats' water supply still intact. In peacetime, ships in distress are usually located before they sink and survivors are not likely to be adrift for very long. In the last war some men were, it is true, left floating for three weeks or more but the great majority were picked up within a few days. Yet victims of shipwreck so consistently tended to anticipate the worst, that instructions had to be issued telling them to drink reasonable amounts of their boat's emergency water supply each day and not to subject themselves to acute thirst until circumstances made it inevitable.

At a rather different level of disaster, there comes to mind an incident in the last war when people under stress deprived themselves of food for reasons that the scientific observer might at first sight take to be illogical. In this instance, however, they were not refusing it because they thought there was still worse deprivation to come, but because they thought it would not give the comfort they wanted. During a bad period of bombing some sympathetic and scientific people in the United States decided to send a nourishing soup to the underfed British. The mixture provided was a balanced composition of vitamins and proteins; its calorific content was all that could be desired. It was, indeed, nutritionally impeccable. Two intelligent dieticians were sent out with a mobile canteen to give it to people sleeping in the underground railway at Shepherds Bush. Unfortunately, when mixed with the appropriate quantity of hot water, the vitamin soup, though meeting every physiological requirement of the human metabolism, was a white paste. And the inhabitants of Shepherds Bush refused to eat it. The dieticians in charge of the canteen, besides being highly qualified in science, were also sensible. They went away and added a pinch of gravy browning, of no nutritional value at all, to the mixture. When they returned, their customers eagerly consumed the soup.

At one time, this sort of thing used to worry the scientific nutritionist, but recently he has begun to appreciate that children at a school are not altogether wise when they 'do' English in one class and history in another and, perhaps, geography in a third—as if they were, as the school timetable implies, separate subjects. Scientific nutrition is growing up and is as I have said before becoming part of a whole list of other sciences: physiology, psychology, sociology. Indeed, if the scientists are not careful, it may become part of one of the humanities again.

Perhaps the modern prescription for nutrition in the 'fall-out zone' suggests which way scientific views are moving. It seems to be becoming recognised in the study of scientific nutrition that almost up to the last extremity of famine and disaster ordinary people go on exhibiting the familiar characteristics of personal idiosyncrasy and human peculiarity that they show so clearly in ordinary life. The scientist now knows that a ration, be it ever so perfect in chemical composition, cannot contribute to well-being if it is not eaten. In one respect, perhaps, this modern enlightenment is to be regretted. By adopting a little cardboard box full of good things to eat as the emergency ration for battling soldiers cut off from their supplies, the British have sacrificed the admiration of foreigners that they enjoyed up to the 1914 war; then, their fighting men carried in their haversacks as protection from disaster a lump of nutritional chocolate in a sealed metal canister bearing on its surface in embossed letters the legend 'only to be opened by express permission of an officer'.

I was once involved by somewhat peculiar circumstances in a series of religious broadcasts. The purpose of the series was to explain how a number of various philosophies of living fitted into the profession of religious dogma. It might, for example, be thought somewhat paradoxical for an individual who considered all life sacred to be employed as a butcher. Or for someone whose persuasion forbade the holding of possessions to be a banker. But in fact this is not so. People are usually able to divide their activities into completely separate compartments. There are numerous veracious accounts of men crying broken-heartedly over a sentimental piece of music or a dead kitten who were capable a moment later of buckling on their revolvers and marching into the street to perpetrate monstrous cruelties and injustices. There are large numbers of people who feel sincere grief and remorse at bringing about the death of a rabbit by means of a virus, myxomatosis, and yet who exult without tremor or qualm at killing rats with Liverpool Virus. But rats are also God's creatures and make excellent and intelligent mothers.

Similarly, scientists whose professional work is a model of system and logic may be found to deal with any other topic than the object of their work with unthinking emotion. Yet science is *not* of itself a 'topic' or a 'subject', it is a way of thinking. It is treated as if it were indeed an occupation or profession. This popular behaviour arises from the very fact that only certain kinds of things are treated scientifically and also because only certain selected, 'professional' people treat these selected things in this scientific way. Yet even so it is not always easy to departmentalise affairs into those that are and those that are not to be considered with scientific logic.

During the course of the last three or four chapters, it will have been noticed that food is a topic that from time to time embarrasses scientists by edging itself into the field where scientific and non-scientific ways of thinking come into contact with each other. In the series of broadcasts to which I have referred one of the speakers said that the fact that he was a scientist—a haematologist, no less—and spent all his time counting stained blood cells under a microscope, had no bearing at all on his religious views. I myself had been sufficiently naïve to admit that if, as a scientific person, one spent one's life assessing evidence and collecting facts, one's belief in a Devil with horns and a tail and a Hell smoking with brimstone, which is the archaic term for the element sulphur, unquestionably tended to be weakened. I may say that this apparently innocuous remark brought down on my head quite a batch of indignant letters.

There is, however, no real cause for surprise at a haematologist whose profession has no bearing on his views of life. Even the great Professor Soddy, discoverer of isotopes, had several hobby-horses that in a lesser man might have been considered to verge on the ridiculous. The food man, however, has much more difficulty in keeping scientific philosophy separate from all the other influences and pressures that affect people in the ordinary course of non-scientific life. Let us take bread as an example that has caused a remarkable amount of heat.

Bread is studied by a number of kinds of scientists, each of whom would be quite content to devote himself to his own particular and interesting research. But he never seems to be left alone to do so. Take the rheologists, for example. Their interest is in the firmness and elasticity of the dough and the bread derived from it. To them, a loaf of bread is similar to a piece of sponge rubber. It consists of a network of protein fibres with starch granules in the interstices between them and enclosing a regular system of bubbles. The purpose of rheological research is to achieve the maximum expansion of the elastic protein balloons so that the membrane of each shall, when finally fixed by the heat of the oven, be thin and delicate in structure. One of the difficulties of achieving this fineness of texture, which is the interest and pleasure of the scientist, is that when the protein fibres are stretched by the kneading of the dough and the expansion of the gas from the yeast they may become, as it were, tangled again before the bread texture is assured. To the scientist, the protein of dough and the protein of hair possess certain similarities. For example, each contains what are called in chemical jargon cross-linkages. It is possible to bend hair, let us say, and then establish its structure in the bent form by joining together opposite members of the molecular cross-links. This is done by the chemistry marketed today in 'home perm' sets. The same chemistry can be used to stabilise the stretched dough proteins, only in this case, the reagents employed are called 'improvers'. But just as soon as the chemist has in this way brought a very difficult and complex research to a satisfactory conclusion and elaborated a highly effective improver, a distinguished physiologist arrives on the scene and publishes *his* elaborate and detailed research to show that bread treated with this particular improver is capable of giving dogs fits.

Then the whole research into the physical structure of elastic dough fibres has to start again, only this time the rheologist whose interest, I repeat, is in the stretching of the protein and the getting of it to stay stretched, has to work in collaboration with another kind of scientist altogether. This is the pharmacologist. The pharmacologist is interested as a general rule in the 'mean lethal dose' of some drug or other. The mean lethal dose is the precise amount that will kill exactly 50 per cent of a group of experimental mice. The problem of bread improvers, however, is not so easy. To start with, the chemical improver itself may not be toxic. It was a part of the wholesome bread-protein itself that, after being acted upon by one im-prover, a gas named Agene, was converted into a different substance that gave Sir Edward Mellanby's dogs fits. The toxicologist is therefore set the job of determining scientifi-cally how much of this stuff will be harmful to people. His task is indeed a difficult one. Although comparatively heroic quantities of bread treated with Agene have been eaten by human volunteers, no clear evidence has come to light that they suffer any harm at all. On the other hand, rabbits, ferrets, mice, rats and monkeys proved to be much more satisfactory experimental animals and a value for the toxic proportion of the active improved-flour substance was established for each.

The dogs convinced the Americans, who gave up Agene almost immediately after its connection with fits was estab-lished. The British were made of stronger stuff and not until the full list of zoological susceptibility had been drawn up did they, after ten years of doubts, change from Agene to chlorine dioxide as the principal improver. But now the scientist is being put to still more arduous trials. He can apply his scientific methods and his objective thinking, and he has done so. The effects of chlorine dioxide on dough elasticity and viscosity have been established—chemically, physically, rheologically. The toxicologist has done his best too. No animal species, it appears, is harmed in any way by bread treated with chlorine dioxide. What more could the layman ask of the scientist? And yet the layman—Everyman, the orig-inal Adam, call him what you will—is not satisfied. His philosophy includes bread as part of life. He refuses to leave alone the bread-scientist who, of course, deals with bread as his scientific subject and not as anything to do with home life.

You will remember my haematologist who stated in his religious broadcast that his scientific pursuits had no bearing on his general views of life outside the blood cells. And now, even after the scientists have done all that was asked of them by way of demonstrating the innocuousness of chlorine dioxide, the French—that is, the whole nation of Franks—decree that they will use no improvers whatever! Neither chlorine dioxide nor anything else. They just do not like the idea of them.

This attitude puts a disciple of science into a false position. It is, of course, impossible to prove a negative. For example, in spite of what *The Ingoldsby Legends* may say, spontaneous combustion does not occur. That is to say, a man cannot take a deep breath, burst into flames and disappear. It is impossible. But suppose someone writes to *The Times* and says 'if people eat bread containing chlorine dioxide they *may* develop symptoms of spontaneous combustion', it is quite impossible to *prove* that this cannot, at some time or another, occur. All that the scientific investigator can do is to say, 'I have examined a group of seven hundred and fourteen people of whom three hundred and twelve were men, four hundred and one were women and one a baby of ten weeks old. These experimental subjects were fed treated bread at a rate equivalent to sixty-two per cent of their total calorie intake over a period of seventeen months. During that time none of them was observed to catch fire nor was there any marked increase in body temperature.' Back comes the answer from non-scientific Everyman, 'Your experiment did not go on long enough. You did not design it right. Do it again and *some* of the people *will* at the very least start to *smoke*.'

This is indeed what occurs. Chlorine dioxide has to be tested on all sorts of animals, by all sorts of methods. No harm has been discovered to come from its use. 'But,' say the French authorities, 'it *might* be bad for you.' So it might.

When we were children we were told that one cannot do two things at once. Even in the nursery we realised that this assertion was false. For example, it can readily be proved that one can eat a banana, read a book and whistle (after a fashion). And in later life there are plenty of ladies who are convinced that they can knit effectively and listen to the wireless at the same time. What our mentors ought to have told us in our youth was that effective *scientific* activity must always be restricted to one topic at a time. The scientists who are devoting themselves to the design of a jet aircraft to travel faster than ever before cannot concern themselves professionally with what they will do with themselves when they get back round the world the day before they started!

The intellectual confusion into which scientists get themselves when they do try to think about two kinds of things at once can be demonstrated by reference to vitamin $B_1$. The existence of this material was first demonstrated in 1898 by a doctor in the Dutch East Indies. He showed that when this 'something' was lacking from their diet, hens developed polyneuritis. And he, that is Dr Eyjkman, also showed that the lack of this same substance was the cause of the widespread and serious Asiatic disease, beri-beri. Starting from these brilliant scientific discoveries, a generation of the consistent, logical and highly technical research for which our age is famous led to the elucidation of the chemical nature of vitamin $B_1$, its function in the biological chemistry of living cells and its subsequent manufacture by synthesis. This is scientific philosophy achieving what it is supremely well fitted to do when first-class minds are available to apply themselves to its problems.

But at this point scientific philosophy bumped up against social philosophy—and unless steps are taken to make them do so, oil and water do not mix. At the time these researches were being brought to their triumphant conclusion, the white bread eaten in Britain by most people contained about a tenth of a milligram of vitamin $B_1$ in 100 grams. Brown bread contained about a quarter of a milligram, or two and a half times as much. There were a whole series of other differences: more 'good' things in brown bread, other B-vitamins, iron and protein, and also more 'bad' things, fibre, phytic acid (an anti-calcium factor) and a tendency to became rancid. But the public debate started with vitamin $B_1$.

It was never suggested that beri-beri had ever been seen in Britain or was likely to occur. But would not more of this new vitamin be good for people? What about the poor? Should not bread, of all foods, be made into a 'complete' food, a compendium of all nourishment? It was not suggested that in the new welfare world of science anyone would be asked to live on bread and water alone. But if they were, should it not be the very *best* bread that science could devise? The debate has swayed to and fro. Scientific evidence of all sorts has been collected. Chemical analysis of different kinds of bread is easy and figures have been collected. But, as with the conceivable harmfulness of chlorine dioxide, the nutritional virtues of different breads cannot be determined in an absolute sense. They are inevitably dependent on the kind of trial used, the experimental animal used—whether rat, hamster, chicken or man. But bread and water is an unsatisfactory diet, as any impoverished student can confirm. And, as has been shown also, in an embarrassing experiment of the Medical Research Council, if bread—even unvitaminised white bread—is used as part of a good mixture, it is an excellent food.

The purport of the last few chapters surely is that science can achieve useful and important things when used to study material food. Science, as a way of thinking, as a kind of philosophy, has been most effective when its beam has been focussed on a small area, that is, when it has been used to think about only one thing at a time. Perhaps its process of collecting facts, constructing hypotheses and verifying these hypotheses by experiment can only be used successfully on material things. Its results certainly have a vast influence on all other parts of life, but we have yet to make general use of scientific methods of thinking and acting in the wider context.

# 9

# CHEMICALS FOR ADAM'S GARDEN

THE Reverend Thomas Malthus made a good deal of stir at the time his *Essay on the principle of population as it affects the future improvement of society* was published. Yet the unforeseen supplies of imported grain and meat from the Americas postponed the clear demonstration of his theory that if populations increase sufficiently, eventually there is not enough to eat. Otherwise he might have got more credit for accurate prophecy in his own lifetime. And the continuous and accelerating increase in the number of people in the world would again have run up against an inadequate food supply before now, in spite of the opening up of new lands, had it not been for a series of major scientific successes.

It is one of the paradoxes of human behaviour that mechanical devices like steam-engines and tin-plate strip mills, rotary printing presses or automatic weaving looms should be acclaimed as major scientific achievements, whereas advances in the scientific understanding of biology—that is, knowledge of the working of life itself—are less appreciated. Yet they represent some of the major triumphs of human thought, and have had great practical significance for mankind as well.

Adam was told to till the earth by the sweat of his brow. At first, if his wheat crop were poor due to disease, he would need to till more ground and sow more wheat or go hungry. Until the day came when he could treat his seed chemically and so destroy on it the micro-organism causing the disease. And within our own generation there has been sudden great flowering of chemical products for Adam's garden. He need no longer use simple and obvious things like copper or arsenic on his food. For instance, tetra-methylthiuram—'thiram', for short—can be used in tiny amounts (2 to 4 lb per acre) to destroy fungus in the soil and thus increase the yield of sugar beet. Peas, beans, carrots and spinach seeds can be treated with it, and after use on flax seed bigger crops obtained.

To prevent scab disease on the apples in his garden, Adam need no longer spray the trees with large quantities of sulphur. In America they use ferric dimethyl-dithio-carbamate— 'ferbam', for short. Ferbam, unluckily, makes a black spray and consequently makes black marks on the apples. In Britain, therefore, we are trying zinc dimethyl-dithio-carbamate— 'ziram', for short, of course—so that we need not see it on the fruit.

There are many substances with long unpronounceable names (some with abbreviations and some without) of varying degrees of toxicity, which are being designed for application to seeds or leaves to cope with the diseases which afflict crop plants. Other even newer chemicals have been invented which the plants draw up through their roots; they are then immune to diseases that they might contract in later life. Tomatoes— and carnations—have been thus rendered resistant to wilt, and strawberries to a disease called 'red core'.

The magnitude of this aspect only of the chemical revolution which is increasing the world's supply of food and at the same time relieving man's labours in the fields is most dramatically—and in some ways most unexpectedly—shown by the fact that the country in which the use of synthetic fungicides seems to have made greatest headway so far is Japan. Most of

the Japanese rice crop is grown in flooded fields under conditions ideally favourable to fungus-born disease. The degree
of loss from this cause was not appreciated until trials of the
new fungicides were started. The young rice plants were
dipped in dithio-carbamate solution before being transplanted.
In some instances, the yield of rice was increased by 30 per
cent. Today, the chemicals are imported by the hundreds of
tons and the *average* amount of extra rice reaped has increased
by more than 10 per cent, equivalent to half the country's
desperate need for imported rice.

The introduction of new, *specific* chemicals—that is chemicals
designed to cope with one special infection—to prevent plant
disease is only part of the scientific revolution we are discussing. There are also new organic chemicals to destroy in-
vading insects. The crude, if romantically named, mixtures of
copper and arsenic known as Paris Green and Bordeaux
Mixture held the field from 1870 and 1885 respectively. Then,
in our own time, came D.D.T., clearing not only man of *his*
vermin, but cabbages, tomatoes, raspberries and gooseberries
of their caterpillars, moths, beetles and sawflies. D.D.T. now has
a number of effective relatives, the so-called chlorinated hydro-
carbons. And, as was done to combat plant diseases, there has
also been a further, scientifically-elegant development of a
group of chemicals which do not have to be sprayed or powdered on to crops in order to kill the insects. A series of organic
phosphorus compounds has been invented which the plants
absorb through their roots and which render all their tissues
toxic to insects. The insects leave them alone and we eat them,
fortified in our mind by the assurance of a monograph of information collected by the World Health Organisation of the
United Nations that they are not toxic to us.

In one of Mr P. G. Wodehouse's fables about the idle rich, a
versatile character, whose promotion of an unsuccessful hair
restorer was proving a financial failure, marketed it with
resounding success as a depilatory. A third important scientific
advance, which is exerting a major influence on our world

today, was—it must in embarrassed humility be admitted—launched in just this manner. In 1953 a report was published in a Berlin journal that certain synthetic organic substances possessed the power of *stimulating* the growth of plant cells. Before very long, however, these substances and others like them—these botanical hair restorers—were being used as weed-killers. The possibility of using them in this way arose from the fact that they affect only certain varieties of plants, including many to which common weeds belong, but do not affect the botanical varieties of which the crops themselves are members. And their killing effect is due to their stimulating the growth only of certain types of cells in the plants that are sensitive to them. Consequently, the orderly growth of these plants is disrupted and they die.

If ever a man looking for a needle in a haystack discovered a crock of gold, it was the biochemist investigating plant growth stimulants who found that he had weed-killers instead. By 1947, the area of crops in Great Britain alone treated with these chemicals could be measured in the hundreds of thousands of acres. By 1952 more than two million acres were covered and in Canada one substance alone, 2-4-dichlorophenoxyacetic acid, was reported as being used to keep the weeds off five to ten million acres of grain!

All kinds of weeds can be eradicated chemically without the need for human sweat: charlock, poppy, ragwort, horsetail, buttercups, rushes. And many types of crop can be safely protected, not only corn but tomatoes, cotton, rice and sugar beet as well.

Weeding by chemistry, although a remarkable way of increasing yields of food and saving work, is not being achieved entirely without difficulty. To start with, you need to be careful what you do with these new and powerful scientific tools. In the United States there have been occasional accidents when weed-killer sprayed on to rice has drifted on to neighbouring fields and seriously damaged the cotton crops growing there. Then again, just as the American house-fly has today managed to adapt itself to a whole battery of the newer insecticides, so has ragwort in some places apparently been able to find a means of defending itself against chlorophenoxyacetic acid herbicides and, after recovering from its initial setback, once again come to grow, as they say, like a weed. Another odd trouble has been the observation that hens which roam about where these weed-killers have been used sometimes fail to lay as many eggs as before and the eggs they do lay do not hatch so well.

Most subtle of all, of course, for the thoughtful scientist is the philosophical question of defining what a weed is. It is all very well to say that it is a plant out of place. But, then, are the wild flowers of the hedgerows out of place there? In Gloucestershire and some other counties they have been studying the effectiveness (from the point of view of a county surveyor, of course) of 'controlling' the vegetation in ditches and on roadside verges by these new techniques. And a spray of selective chemical weed-killer will exterminate the wild flowers as well as the other plants you cannot eat.

This silent chemical revolution in food production and in saving old Adam from the labours of the field has remarkable possibilities. Systematic herbicides can be designed not only to kill some plants and leave others alone, but also to affect only certain parts of a particular plant. For instance, one has been used with some success to cause the leaves of the cotton plant to fall off so that the cotton can be harvested more effectively by machinery. The same principle is being studied in Kenya where 2-4-5-trichlorophenoxyacetic acid is being sprayed from aeroplanes to cause the leaves of a whole range of trees and shrubs to fall off so that the tsetse fly shall be prevented from sheltering under them.

The most remarkable feature of this whole business, this scientific advance, is its speed and its silence. We seem to have looked round and found it suddenly upon us with all its extraordinary implications: the fungicides, the insecticides and plant-growth-stimulating chemicals turned weed-killers.

It is a happy event that the great practical significance of what has been achieved is, on this occasion, coupled with the considerable philosophical significance of the discoveries we have been describing. The invention of a steam-engine or an aeroplane had an immense practical effect but neither machine represented much in the way of an advance in human thought. One could imagine that if a Chinese philosopher had happened to design either machine he might have constructed it for the amusement of his friends but would hardly have used it as a means of revolutionising civilised life.

The scientific developments that we have been discussing in this chapter represent a remarkable degree of biological control, that is, the control of certain chosen living cells in the presence of others whose normal life remains unaffected. It is salutary once again to recall that the potent effect exerted by micro-organisms on larger living creatures, whether they be animals or plants, was first recognised only eighty odd years ago by Louis Pasteur. And yet today, starting from Pasteur's original shaft of intellectual brilliance we are able not only to identify the micro-organisms causing the smut diseases of wheat or the scab on apples or the fungus diseases of rice but also to kill the living disease cells without harming the tissues of the grain or fruit to which the specially designed chemical antiseptic is applied.

Development of the power to kill has been a consistent feature in the history of man. To the natural philosopher the attention given by men to killing other men is a dull subject. Few people can seriously interest themselves in the squalid seventeenth-century quarrels of insignificant Scottish clans, and the same type of activity multiplied to the larger scale of recent wars is equally uninteresting. The biological struggle between the human species and the insects is, however, a topic worthy of intelligent thought.

H. G. Wells once wrote a vivid and frightening story called *The Kingdom of the Ants*. A broken-down gunboat commanded by an incompetent middle-aged captain with a Scottish engineer and a crew of South American militia was sent a ten-day journey up the Amazon. There they found a township on the verge of the jungle forests deserted of all human life. It was, however, inhabited by ants of a new variety allied to the leaf cutters. Their behaviour was commanded by soldier ants of high intelligence and equipped with poison carried by certain of their numbers. Their advance through the jungle showed every sign of being a planned migration. They showed themselves capable of tunnelling under rivers of considerable size— and they experienced no difficulty in despatching the chief mate of the gunboat who was sent by the commander to reconnoitre the situation. The gallant commander then fired the brass gun with which his vessel was equipped and, after this ineffectual demonstration, withdrew down river.

But it is not necessary to call upon Mr Wells's imagination to appreciate the evenness of the struggle between these two powerful groups of creatures, men and insects. Part of the history has been told by Zinsser in his classical book *Rats, Lice and History*. In it he recounts some of the great plagues that have ravaged humanity as mere incidents in the efforts of the diminutive louse to find space to live a lousely life. Mankind now appears to have achieved victory in this battle by inventing D.D.T. Another contest against an insect has not yet been determined: there are still territories where man cannot live as master because of the tsetse fly. The biblical plagues of locusts are also still to be reckoned with. Mankind has the scientific knowledge to settle this battle, as was demonstrated by the entomologists of the Middle East Supply Centre during World War II. Unfortunately the political common sense to agree to do so appears to be lacking. Against this background, the new scientific knowledge of how to kill insects that would otherwise eat the plants we need for food ourselves is a worthy achievement.

These scientific advances are only a part of a larger understanding of life. Biologists, and philosophers for that matter, have for long been interested in the respective influences of

heredity and environment on living creatures and on the cells
of which they are composed. The fungicides that attack the
plant disease organisms, the insecticides that destroy the para-
sites and the chemical weed-killers that cut down the competi-
tors of the growing crops all bring their influence to bear on
environment.

The single biggest influence we wield on the environment of
growing things, whether they be babies, pigs or fields of corn,
is that of nutrition. So far as man is concerned, the most important contribution that natural philosophy, as expressed
through chemistry, has made to nutrition has been to increase
total food production. The fundamental nutritional deficiency
in the world today is, as it has always been, a deficiency of
calories, that is to say, too little to eat. In 1946 a Cambridge
scientist wrote as a preface to one of his papers a review of the
history of human hunger. He started merrily with a report by
Hesiod of a famine in 700 B.C., continued with a circumstantial
account from the Second Book of Kings and, after noticing
586 other references to the scientific literature, ended with the
medical account of the famine in north Holland in 1945.

Living plant cells, like the living cells of animals, must be
nourished. Plants create calories from sun and air and consequently do not need to be supplied with them, but they
possess other wants. True, science has systematised the knowledge of plant nutrition and extended its bounds, but we must
always avoid the danger of believing that we moderns have
done it all.

*We think our fathers fools, so wise we grow,*
*Our wiser sons no doubt will think us so.*

References to manuring occur in Chinese and Egyptian
literature as well as in that of Greece and Rome. Liming is
also of some antiquity and ground bones and guano have been
used at least since the beginning of the nineteenth century.
Since the time of the field experiments of John Bennett Lawes
at Rothamsted and his patent for superphosphate taken out in

1842, the use of 'artificials' has become one of the great examples of the application of scientific thought to the practical improvement of mankind—or if not the improvement at least the preservation of mankind from hunger.

Sir William Crookes, in his presidential address to the British Association in 1898, calculated that if the supply of wheat was to keep pace with the growth of the world population, it would be necessary to increase the yield of grain from the then level of 12·7 bushels per acre up to 20 bushels per acre by 1928. To do this, said Sir William, would require a total dressing of twelve million tons of nitrate of soda, a fantastic quantity in the scientific eyes of 1898. Today, of course, more than twice as much can be made each year in factories that 'fix' nitrogen from the air, and the total manufacture of chemical fertilisers in 1950 was about forty million tons. In addition to this, nitrate is mined in Chile, while whole Pacific islands composed of the accumulated droppings of myriads of prehistoric seagulls are carted away to keep up the productivity of Australian farms.

But blood will out, as they used to write in the romantic novels of a hundred years ago. In these stories, environment was nothing. The hero, stolen from his cot as an infant, spent two or three hundred pages under conditions of poverty, hardship and squalor. This unfavourable environment, however, did him no harm. When in the last chapter he was recognised by a characteristic birthmark as being the long-lost son of the earl, he instantly reassumed his rightful station, demonstrated by his bearing and manner that he was indeed a gentleman of refined taste and sensibility and showed no trace of having picked up bad habits or a cockney accent during the long years spent as a kitchen porter in Stoke Newington.

Paradoxically enough, although the environmental influences brought to bear on plants by the genius of science have had important results, as we have already described, the greatest increase in food supply has been achieved by influencing hereditary rather than environmental factors. The yield of wheat has, it is true, been substantially increased by the understanding of the requirement of plants for nitrogen, phosphorus and potash and the invention of means to supply these needs as artificial fertilisers. Nevertheless, the major increase in the world's food supply has been due to the science of genetics. By the direct application of genetical principles it has been found possible to breed varieties of wheat that are capable of growing in parts of the world where conditions are too dry and the season too short for normal varieties to thrive. In Canada, for example, enormous areas of what were barren plains in the west and north of the country can now be used to produce these new varieties of wheat. It is the 'blood lines' of these strains, that is, their hereditary background, that has been the dominant feature in the practical success of this application of scientific philosophy to practical affairs. But the chosen strains do not possess their noble blood by accident. It is put into them by the logical application of genetical science. And not only can breeding give Marquis wheat the ability to grow in countries where no wheat grew before. It can do more. Between 1925 and 1935, the annual loss of wheat from a disease, rust, in Manitoba and Saskatchewan was thirty-five million bushels. Chemical fungicides to remove rust disease from the environment were ineffective. A cross-bred grain from the irregular union of two separate Marquis matings was made. The offspring of this union was called Thatcher and it is resistant to the most damaging of the fungus diseases afflicting wheat. Plant breeding can help to increase food supplies in other ways. Wheat, for example, can be modified to grow with a short stalk, long enough to allow it to be garnered with a combine harvester but not so long that it would be beaten down by wind or rain.

That the science of genetics could, by increasing the world's wheat supply, have thus so significantly contributed to human nutrition would have come as a surprise to Thomas Malthus. Of all men, the clergy tend to be most homocentric. Living creatures to them are people only, not lice or plants. To the natural philosopher, be he a biologist at large, a geneticist or a chemist, the mechanism of plant genetics is as worthy of investigation as are the genetics of a winning Derby horse or a man. And genetics is being increasingly recognised as a field for *chemical* study.

A gene is part of a chromosome which behaves as a unit in the physiology of a cell. In certain types of chromosomes that have been very closely studied there appear to be about 30,000 genes in each. And each gene is approximately the same size as a chemical molecule of protein. Furthermore, it is now clear that the way genes affect the appearance and character of the living creatures whose destiny they control is through the exercise of a specific *chemical* function.

In 1936, Rose Scott-Moncrieff in Cambridge was investigating the factors controlling the anthocyanin pigments in plants—and what better pursuit could be conceived for a natural philosopher than to study the colours of flowers? As a result of this work it was soon possible to give an account of thirty-five different genes concerned in the variation in colours between different kinds of flowers. Each of these genes was found to control a precise chemical difference between the pigments producing the varied colours. For example, one gene caused the anthocyanin molecule to be oxidised at one particular place—and the flower colour to be affected accordingly. Another gene added a $CH_2$ grouping at another part of the molecule. And so on.

The Abbé Mendel founded the science of genetics by studying the colours of sweet peas. The principles by which coloured sweet pea parents influence the colours of their offspring are now known to be the same as those by which animal parents transmit their inheritance to *their* progeny. Now it appears that the Mendelian genes, which are the active agents carrying the characteristics we inherit, attain their results by a specific chemical effect—and thus produce improved wheat, or perhaps an improved man.

Of all the chemicals in Adam's garden, the one most worthy of the attention of the philosophical scientist is Adam himself.

## 10

# MICROBE CHEMISTRY

SCIENCE has been used very effectively to do practical, industrial things, to make steam-engines and motor-cars and electric lamp bulbs. We have also seen how scientific thinking can be applied to problems of human nutrition and food production. These are, of course, aspects of applied biology. But having discovered how living cells work and how they manufacture for themselves the substances they need for their own well-being, it has not taken us long to bend the biology of other creatures to our benefit.

There is a well-known story of a man who furnished a room with all the luxuries of civilised living. There were ornaments on the mantelpiece, carpets, curtains and furniture of all sorts; the table was laid with the finest cutlery and glass and covered with a damask cloth. There was a piano and a gramophone; bookcases filled with bound volumes lined the walls and a bright fire burned in the grate. Into this room the man introduced a chimpanzee. Then he locked the door and went away. After a while he crept back to observe what the monkey was doing. With the greatest caution he applied his eye to the keyhole. And all he saw was—another eye.

In 1665, a thirty-year-old Englishman, Robert Hooke, who

combined mechanical skill, inventive genius and extraordinary scientific insight to a high degree, published a book, *Micrographia*. Just as Galileo's publications of 1600 had, by the aid of the newly invented telescope, opened men's eyes to new and very large worlds in the heavens, so Hooke brought to life a new and unsuspected universe of the very small. One of the first drawings he made of this fairy world that he now saw existing in the very same living-space as his own was of the compound eyes of a dragonfly. Eyes which, like those of the dog in the fairy-story, were as large as cartwheels; although they had been looking at us for ages they were being seen by us for the first time.

The first men to fly did so partly for fun—as a matter of spirit—and partly to see whether flying could be done; whether, that is, it was scientifically feasible. Soon, however, aviation became a matter of everyday commerce. Space travel looks as if it may never enjoy even a brief interval as an achievement of human thought and fire but will start right off as a businesslike affair of economics and politics. The little world of micro-organisms has been exploited almost as soon as it has been discovered. Nevertheless, its discovery and use is a remarkable example of scientific achievement which has not received the general recognition it deserves.

The initial spark of intuition that started the whole train of discovery must be attributed to Louis Pasteur, then engaged as a chemist in the humdrum task of investigating the reason why wine went sour. From his original notion that the yeast first seen by Antoni van Leeuwenhoek in 1680 as rounded egg-shaped bodies, and only recognised as being a living thing by Cagniard de la Tour in France and Schwann in Germany in 1835, was the active creature that was changing sugar into alcohol in beer wort came the whole science of microbiology as we know it today.

It is interesting to remember that the inhabitants of the invisible underworld that enjoy the earth with us are as varied in size one with another as we are in comparison with the animals of our visible world. For example, a yeast cell is one of the elephants of the microscopical underworld; if it were as big as a flea, a man would have to be 600 feet tall to maintain his existing advantage. Beside it, there are bacteria causing gangrene. They are as big as horses. The psittacosis organism capable of transmitting parrot disease is the size of a guinea pig. A scale smaller are another whole group of living things, the viruses. The influenza virus is as big as a humming-bird or a small mouse compared with our lumbering elephantine yeast cell, but the foot-and-mouth disease organism, powerful and destructive though it is, would only seem as large as a gnat.

A philosopher, it is said, is a man in armour. He can defend himself against the troubles that beset an individual because his philosophy teaches him to expect the sort of things that life can bring. The scientist, the natural philosopher of today, carries equipment more up-to-date than armour. Galileo, Hooke and van Leeuwenhoek in the seventeenth century taught him to study the nature of miniature life with an optical microscope and the great Newton showed him what kind of things light rays were that were focussed through the compound lenses of his instrument. But light rays are too coarse to allow us to see the detailed structure of living matter or to identify the smallest living beings there are. So, in our own day, we needed to invent the electron microscope. This is similar in principle to the optical miscroscope except that it uses beams of electrons instead of beams of light. And these beams are focussed by suitably arranged magnetic systems in place of the lenses that control the optical system of a conventional instrument. An electron microscope allows one, if not to see a virus and its organs of locomotion, at least to see a photograph of it.

The moral law says that all men are born free and equal, only some are more equal than others. Perhaps the greatest philosophical discovery of biological science in the twentieth century is that what constitutes life on earth, whether it be in a King Solomon, a fruit fly or a micro-organism, is chemically the same thing, although in some bacteria it is a little different. In the words of Szent-Györgyi quoted in the next chapter, the energy for living is obtained either by combusting some fuel material in one's cells with the oxygen in air, or by the splitting of the material into parts. And in both processes, a remarkably similar set of biochemical tools is used by all sorts of creatures, large or small, warm or cold, microscopic or macroscopic.

When a man is in a great hurry to get energy and has no time, or for some other reason, is unable to use the more efficient process of combining his blood's sugar with oxygen —for example, if he is trying to run a hundred yards in nine seconds—instead of combusting sugar he merely splits it and lactic acid accumulates in his blood. Yeast, which after all has been *seen* down a microscope since the seventeenth century although it was only *recognised* in the nineteenth, can respire like we do. But, as has also been noticed since the days of Noah, when it splits its fuel instead of fully burning it, it produces, not lactic acid like a man, but alcohol.

For quite a substantial period of historical time, yeasts were among the comparatively few members of the microbiological world that we human beings made use of. We collected alcohol, their waste product, and drank it for its toxic properties as wine. The other by-product, carbon dioxide gas, has been employed to leaven bread. But the use of yeast in this way derives from the time before micro-organisms were domesticated. Nowadays, we do not get eggs from a jungle fowl capable of laying two or three clutches a year. We take them from a carefully bred bird that will produce three hundred eggs a year—and these will be larger and more regular and, surprisingly enough, more nutritious than those from the jungle fowl. In just the same way yeasts have been domesticated, although it takes ten million of these elephants of the microbe world all standing shoulder to shoulder (a truly Kiplingesque conception) to be just visible to us as a speck on the back of our thumb-nail.

Yeast, this oldest of man's micro-friends, leavens his dough.

He uses its excretion, alcohol, to drink; or, as industrial alcohol, for a motor fuel, as a solvent or as a raw material for a host of manufactured chemical products. Nowadays, even its breath, carbon-dioxide gas, is compressed into a solid and used for making ice-cream, or cooling machine tools.

But we are not satisfied to stop at using the natural life-chemicals of the yeast—the carbon dioxide and the alcohol—as major industrial commodities. Scientific knowledge of the mechanism of life now enables us to interfere with it to our own advantage—and the interference about which I wish to write now had that most potent of human motives, war. The chemical reactivity of sodium sulphite is such that it could be deduced that it would poison yeast in a particular way. And in fact when the experiment was tried it was found that it did so. Now, if one goes into the right chemical factories and looks in the right place, there can be seen great vats in which yeast intoxicated with sodium sulphite is struggling to 'breathe'. It cannot grow in the presence of the sulphite but it does not die. Instead of producing alcohol, its major by-product becomes glycerol. A harmless, sweet-tasting, sticky liquid, it might be said, sometimes called glycerine and used in cough lozenges. And why be sentimental about using our knowledge of the chemistry of life in this way since yeasts cannot feel? Is it not a triumph for the scientist that the glycerol is converted into explosives of war?

In studying the basic biochemistry by which living cells live, it is legitimate to argue from what happens to white rats and guinea pigs to what is likely to happen to men. And with only a comparatively few reservations, it can be assumed that, by and large, what goes on in the cells of microbes will also be occurring in our own cells. Yet there are certain differences which, although they may be accounted of minor importance in bio-chemistry, often have an important practical significance. For instance, one strain of bacterium may produce a small amount of a special and peculiar chemical substance. *Clostridium botulinum* lives in soil and is so far undomesticated but it is well known for the special compound it produces. There is a report in a scientific text-book of a woman who opened a container of bottled string beans that she was going to cook for the family's dinner. Noticing a funny smell about them, she took a piece of raw bean and put it in her mouth. It tasted a 'bit off', so she threw the rest of the bottle away. But the piece she had tasted had contained the chemical toxin produced by *Clostridium botulinum*, one of the most poisonous substances known, and in five hours she was dead.

*Clostridium acetobutylicum* is a member of the same family as *Clostridium botulinum* but mercifully is not endowed with its peculiar chemical habits. This organism *has* been domesticated because it was observed that instead of getting energy by breaking up sugar molecules into alcohol (that is, ethyl alcohol), a two-carbon substance, it varied the process and produced butanol (a four-carbon substance) plus acetone and a miscellaneous collection of other materials. This peculiarity in behaviour was first observed in 1861 by Pasteur but it was only in 1910 that the idea occurred to one or two reflective scientists that *Clostridium acetobutylicum* might be tamed and put to work to produce butanol commercially. In fact, it needed once again the spur of war before the biochemical philosophers achieved an industrial process out of a biological mechanism. And the operation was put into action not primarily for the butanol but to help relieve the shortage of acetone that was hampering the manufacture of cordite used to propel rifle bullets! Today there are large factories in Great Britain, the United States, Canada and elsewhere in which thousands of tons of acetone and of butanol (often used to make synthetic rubber), produced incidentally by *Clostridium acetobutylicum* in its struggle to live without air, are collected by mankind and put to all sorts of industrial purposes. And just as with other domestic animals—the milk cow, the bacon pig or the champion hen—we have employed scientific specialists to breed and train the organisms. They have now spent years hunting the invisible world—or perhaps it would be better to call it the subvisible world—for *Clostridium* in such apparently improbable places as the roots of French beans, in stored grain, even on the skin of gooseberries, in search of strains that will produce more acetone and butanol when brought into a factory and fed sugar in the form of, say, molasses.

Of all the drugs manufactured by the manufacturing druggists of the Western world today, penicillin is the one of greatest commercial importance. It even outstrips aspirin. And yet the fact that it was being produced by a mould floating invisibly in the atmosphere was only discovered thirty-odd years ago by Fleming in his laboratory at St Mary's Hospital, London, W.2. The story of the discovery that this particular and rather unusual microbe, *Penicillium notatum*, was making this peculiar and most complicated chemical has been told many times. But it is nevertheless worth repeating again.

When a microbiologist is studying microbes he usually gets them to grow in a shallow layer of gelatin, or similar material, in a glass dish. Each single microbe grows on the gelatin until, where one microbe was before—only visible under a microscope—a colony develops that can be seen with the naked eye. If the microbiologist then picks off this colony with a needle and grows *it* in a flask of sugar or gelatin or broth of some kind, instead of having a mixture of different microbes he has only one sort. Now in 1929, Professor Fleming was doing this very thing. He was growing a mixture of bacteria in one of the shallow dishes that bacteriologists call 'Petrie plates'. By accident, however, a mould was flying about in the air of his laboratory and happened to settle on the dish. And there, like a cuckoo's egg in a nest of sparrows, it 'hatched' and grew into a colony along with the colonies of the microbes Professor Fleming wanted to grow. This sort of thing is a common laboratory accident. And Professor Fleming's first reaction was to do what any normal research worker would have done under the circumstances: that is, put the Petrie dish into the sink, wash it up and start again. But then he stopped and did what normal research workers often do not do—he looked at the 'spoiled' plate and he began *to think about* what he saw. And the conclusion he reached was that the mould that had accidentally got in, *Penicillium notatum*, was preventing any other microbe growing near it. This meant, so he reasoned, that it must be producing a chemical of some sort that stopped other microbes growing near it. This unknown chemical he called 'penicillin'.

Of course, the discovery that penicillin existed was not the end of the story. A great deal of hard work was done by a number of people, just to show that it was a difficult substance to purify and isolate for use. Indeed, it was difficult to deal with and so easily destroyed in the laboratory that for eight years the idea of making use of it at all was abandoned. Then the war began in 1939. Among a number of others Professor Florey and Dr Chain in Oxford, realising how very important it could be in preventing infection in war wounds, began to undertake a serious attempt to get *Penicillium notatum* to grow in such a way that reasonable amounts of the remarkable chemical it produced could be obtained.

In 1944, the first commercial supplies of penicillin became available. By 1951, the value of the penicillin produced in the United States alone, which is still the biggest manufacturing country, was 137 million dollars. Today, it is used for all sorts of medical purposes, in some of which it has changed the entire character of a previously killing disease, pneumonia for example, in others of which it does no good at all and is tossed in by the physician for luck (sometimes good luck, sometimes not). It is employed in massive quantities as an addition to pig food or poultry ration to exert its effect, sometimes useful, sometimes doubtful, on the micro-organisms in the digestive tracts of farm livestock. And once the discovery of an antibiotic substance produced by a mould had been made by one of those flashes of intuition upon which the progress of science depends, the swarms of us lesser philosophers descended on all the likely and unlikely moulds and micro-organisms to see whether *they* also make something of use to ourselves. And some of them do, as is witnessed by the streptomycins and aureomycins and chloramphenicols and many more.

A rather different example of the domestication of a wild microbe and its harnessing to the industrial chariot of man is contained in the modern history of *Eremothecium ashbii*. In 1928 a French botanist was studying a disease affecting the cotton plants in French Equatorial Africa. He discovered that this disease was due to a microbe parasite, *Eremothecium ashbii*. The object of the exercise was to get rid of the microbe and grow healthy cotton. Other French botanists got drawn into the research and in 1935 they noticed that under some circumstances the microbe contained quite large crystals of a yellow substance. They were curious about these crystals and set out —purely in the interests of scientific enquiry—to discover what they were made of. What was their surprise and, I may say, that of the rest of the scientific world, when it was discovered that they were nuggets, as it were, of a pure vitamin. This vitamin, now called riboflavin, was at one time known as vitamin $B_2$. At once, researchers in Japan, in Switzerland and in the United States set to work to see how *Eremothecium ashbii* could be tamed. It was taken away from its natural habitat on cotton plants in Africa and, just like a wild animal brought into a zoo, it was fed on a variety of artificial diets in an attempt to discover what it would grow on in captivity. Many kinds of regimen were used, ranging from sugar with a mixture of pure chemical substances added, all the way to a thin broth made of lentils. But today this micro-organism shares the fate of the penicillin microbe and is grown in great vessels in large factories. And when it has been grown the vitamin is extracted from it and can be sold by the pound. In 1948, more than 130,000 lb. were manufactured in the United States alone and used either to improve human diets, as a medicine for people suffering from vitamin deficiency, or in animal and poultry-feeding rations.

We are generally aware that the whole of biological creation is in a state of dynamic equilibrium. If the Red Indians are given rifles and with them exterminate the buffalo the equilibrium between buffalo and Red Indians is upset. If the European rabbit is introduced into the Australasian continent, its numbers will increase until a biological balance is once more struck. And man too is in balance with the microbes. They break down his sewage and fix nitrogen for his crops. Some sewage organisms even do work for him.

*Methanobacter omelianskii* can split the molecular substance of wet dead leaves on marshes and produce the inflammable gas methane as one of the by-products of the reaction. Sometimes the ignited gas flickering in the twilight will give a 'will-o'-the wisp' or 'jack o' lantern'. The idea of using this gas to do work was first brought to practical fruition, so far as I am aware, in 1897 when the gas coming off sewage tanks in the somewhat unexpected environment of a leper colony in Matunga in Bombay was collected and used to drive a gas-engine. At about the same time the municipal authorities in Exeter in Devonshire used this same microbe chemistry for heating and lighting. In 1927, the engines used to work the sewage disposal plant in Birmingham were run on the methane produced in the plant itself, while in Essen the gas was piped into the town mains for cooking and lighting.

All this business we have been discussing in the few pages of this chapter surely represents a substantial achievement in thinking. Although Antoni van Leeuwenhoek first saw the yeast microbe in 1680 it was only a hundred years ago (when railways had already been invented and the modern industrial age was getting into full swing) that Louis Pasteur realised that there was a world of invisibly small creatures all around us. And not only did he appreciate—against strongly entrenched contrary opinion, be it said—that these creatures could harm us unless we either tamed, confined or exterminated them; just as we have tamed, confined or exterminated the European lion, the wild boar and the wolf of the larger visible world; but he also had the intuition to see that the invisible creatures might be domesticated and be made to yield *their* milk or other appropriate secretion. Now, dotted about all over the country we can see the gaunt walls and towering chimney stacks of industrial alcohol plants, penicillin factories, manufactories of industrial solvents, or sewage works—and remember that they are all carried on the toiling shoulders of the little microbe people who live in the interstices of the world in which we live and think.

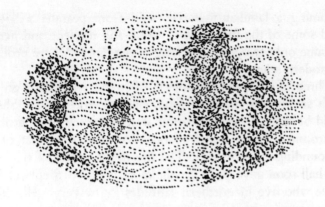

## 11

# AIR

NOWADAYS, in this age of science, we expect the food we eat to be processed. Indeed, without the modern developments in artificial fertilisers to increase crop yields, without the discoveries of plant genetics to create varieties of wheat capable of growing in northern latitudes of Canada where no wheat ever grew before, without chemical insecticides and systematic weed-killers to prevent losses there would not be enough food to go round. And without the techniques of canning, refrigeration, dehydration and preservation by various means it would not be possible to distribute successfully the food we have to the crowded populations of our present urban civilisation.

Similarly, with clothing, none of the natural fibres which we use in textiles are left in their native state. Wool is defatted, bleached, dyed and blended. The production of cotton is even more technical. The bacteriology of flax wretting is a subject for a Ph.D. thesis. And beyond all these, of course, we now have so-called 'man-made', or artificial, fibres. Artificial silk— or as it is now politely termed, 'rayon'—made from sawdust has been with us for a considerable time; nylon is gradually becoming a familiar material; ardil from peanuts will soon fulfil some of the functions of wool; and terylene and perlon, to name only two, are knocking at the door. All are products of modern science.

Three of the primary objects of man's endeavour on this earth are the provision of food, clothing and shelter. Shelter could be defined as the creation around oneself of an artificial environment more suited to one's comfort than that of the surrounding out-of-doors. The fire in the centre of the baronial hall soon gave place to the more civilised fireplace. But, as we who live in northern latitudes know very well, this is not a completely satisfactory answer to the problem of providing comfortable surroundings. It is interesting to recall that during the eighteenth and nineteenth centuries a great deal of scientific effort was devoted to the improvement of fireplaces. Many of the earlier patents deal with improved chimney-pots and other devices to prevent fires from smoking.

Today, it is reasonable to believe that even the long-suffering British are becoming dissatisfied with a system of warming the environment that, while mitigating the more extreme rigours of the climate, fails to avoid a large measure of cold and draughty discomfort and is accompanied each year by a wholesale destruction of water-pipes by frost and a serious contamination of the outdoor atmosphere. Just as we apply science and technology to our food and to our clothing, so can we with equal logic apply the same kind of modern knowledge to the air we consume. Civilised man considers that almost all of his food needs to be processed *and* cooked. Will he not in the future refuse to take his air raw?

Before the 1939–45 war about 200 million dollars' worth of machinery for air conditioning was sold in the United States each year. Most of this, however, was for factories and commercial buildings. By 1953, the magnitude of the business had expanded to 1,700 million dollars—more than eight times as much—and about a quarter of this was for domestic use. The characteristic protuberance of a 'packaged' air cooler sticking out from the window-sill in a block of flats has become in America as important a social symbol and as essential a feature of the good life as has a television aerial for the British semi-detached home.

There are various types of domestic air-conditioning plants on the market in America. A small, two-horsepower unit—the so-called 'window-box'—costs about £100 and deals with the air in a single room. A bigger one of about fifteen horsepower, looking like a giant refrigerator, will cope with a small hotel. And then there are several types of central air-conditioning systems which will cool the whole atmosphere of a private house in summer and warm it in winter. It is estimated that, just as all good houses in the United States are now equipped with central heating, within five years at least half the new houses built will have air conditioning as well.

It is only within the last hundred years that we have seriously begun to apply science to our lives and now that, at last, after dealing with food and clothing we are beginning to cope with the circumambient atmosphere which is our shelter, things are bound to go with a rush. A basic premise of science is that nothing is ever lost. For example, if one warms a room with a radiator, the heat gained by the room is merely transferred from the water in the pipes. Contrariwise, when the air in a refrigerator is cooled, the warmth from the air is merely taken up by the coils in the refrigerator. This basic and simple principle having been recognised, it was merely a matter of scientific thinking for there to be invented a new device about which we are certain to hear a great deal more before long. This is the so-called 'heat pump'.

One of the first of these to be installed was in the Festival Hall in London. When the hall gets too hot, the machinery is put to work and the heat is, as it were, pumped out. Because science decrees that nothing can disappear into nothing, the heat has to go somewhere—and it goes to warm the river Thames. Should the Hall be too cold, the pump can warm it by going into reverse and extracting some heat from the river. For a private house, a machine of the same sort is now available, capable of pumping heat *out* of the refrigerator in the kitchen, and hence keeping the food cold, and delivering it into the drawing-room which is by this means kept warm. Unfortunately, up to the present, heat pumps are still somewhat expensive to run in the domestic home. Nevertheless, when, as we soon must, we overcome the human inertia which we have inherited from our pre-scientific ancestors, the equipment for processing the air around us is at hand.

The educated man's views as to whether air is or is not good for him have fluctuated quite widely during recent times. In the early nineteenth century, Emma's father, Mr Woodhouse, was horrified that anyone should be so rash as to open a window, whereas in the following century members of the same class of English society caused consternation throughout Europe and beyond by insisting in the teeth of local opposition that railway carriage windows should never be closed— except, of course, when passing through a tunnel. Scientific opinion has also shown some variability. Barely a generation ago there were serious discussions as to whether a place was 'relaxing' or 'bracing'. And many a seaside resort made great play with the healthful smell of ozone on its beach until it gradually became apparent that it was not ozone but decaying seaweed.

The British, belatedly following in the wake of all other civilised countries of similar latitude, have at last reached the conclusion that it is reasonable to make the air in which they live comfortable. It has been estimated that, judging from the present rate of progress, Americans born in 1960 may expect to spend their entire lives in an air-conditioned atmosphere— at home, at school, at work and in all places of entertainment at every season of the year. The Anglo-Saxons do not expect to achieve so complete a degree of technical control so soon, nor may they wish to do so. There is cause, however, to take the matter seriously.

Disagreeable features of untreated air arise from causes

other than the weather. The British domestic hearth, with its allegedly cheerful coal-fire, renowned though it may be for nourishing solid virtues, consumes a great deal of solid fuel and contributes some 900,000 tons—about half the total—to the annual output of British smoke. The 'smokeless zones' established by the city fathers of Manchester, Coventry and other places only apply to industry and commerce and have little concern with home fires.

As a general rule the inhabitants of great towns just manage to establish a workable *modus vivendi* with their urban atmosphere. In the London area, for example, the *normal* concentration of smoke between Westminster and Beckton in December may reach seventy milligrams of smoke per cubic metre and twenty parts of sulphur dioxide per 100 million without causing comment. But in December 1953, a series of meteorological coincidences caused the smoke and sulphur dioxide to increase five-fold and 4,000 people were killed. Although some of these were old people who, as was pointed out by certain commentators who wished to avoid causing alarm, belonged to the category of those 'who were going to die in any event'— others were infants or merely sufferers from bronchitis.

It was recorded by John Evelyn some time ago that the British wrap their cities in 'a hellish and dismal cloud of seacoale'. In spite of a series of ineffective legislative gestures since Evelyn's time, culminating in the Beaver report of 1954 which confirms the fact that air pollution is an 'evil which should no longer be tolerated', it is probable that the degree of contamination has grown heavier through the centuries. The blackness of the buildings and the state of the atmosphere would have shocked our pre-industrial forefathers very much. It is fortunate that the twentieth-century citizens can at least still be shocked at their predecessors' drains.

Artificial textiles created by science are here to stay to supplement the wool and cotton, flax and leather of agriculture. In certain respects, nylon and the rest are an improvement on nature. Processed foods are safer, more stable and often more nourishing than the natural article. The taste of tinned pineapple is not quite *the same* as that of the raw fruit but many people consider it is *nicer*. With analogies such as these ready to hand, we surely cannot avoid the conclusion that processed air is safer, more agreeable, more sweet smelling and in every way *better* than the medium to be found in the twentieth-century out-of-doors. The domestic air-conditioner is obviously going to take its place with the refrigerator, the washing-machine, the infra-red cooker and the television as essential to civilised life. All the evidence shows that in the new technological age the widespread suspicion of fresh air is justified.

Science has been applied to the study of air in many other ways than just to consider its qualities as a comfortable medium for human existence. Air has been liquefied and used as a refrigerant for substances that require to be cooled to low temperatures. It is now being used as a fuel for rockets. The separate components of air have been boiled off one by one in just the same way that the brandy is boiled off wine when it is distilled. And so the oxygen, the nitrogen, the argon, the helium and other rare gases, only discovered to exist on earth after they had already been identified by their spectra as existing in the sun and other stars, have been separated.

It is a very characteristic feature of scientific thinking, as I have mentioned once or twice before, to consider facts and observations in the absolute, as it were. We ordinary mortals are always modifying the way we recognise facts by a whole series of extraneous considerations that really have no bearing on the matter in hand. 'My dear,' says the grand lady referring to her party of the night before, 'there was *nobody* there at all. But nobody!' She does not mean, of course, that the room was empty but merely that there was nobody present whom she considered to be important. For a very long time the brick-maker and the concrete manufacturer, like the society leader at her party, would have ignored glass as being merely something to look through or make bottles out of. To the scientist, its tensile strength, compressibility, its weight and heat-resistant qualities can be assessed along with the qualities of other substances to see whether it is fitted to be used as a building material.

Nowadays, the physical properties of air have been assessed in a like manner and it is being used as just one more raw material on the basis of its mechanical strength. At one time the possibility of constructing a heavier-than-air machine capable of flying was considered to be as remote as the idea of an iron ship. But the successful experiment having been carried out, the scientists have now collected a large amount of data on the precise properties of air as a supporting medium.

Air, like concrete, does not possess much tensile strength but is valuable on account of its resistance to compression. Modern automatic processes in industry require a variety of mechanical devices to which power is transmitted in such a way that they can pick up, put down, turn over and generally move about the components that are undergoing the process of manufacture. These tongs and grabs and pushers and pullers can be powered by means of rods or wires. But in many circumstances it is found more convenient to move them about by rods (or columns, if you prefer to think of them as such) of air. At one time the brakes of railway trains and heavy commercial vehicles were worked by means of metal rods or wire cables. Nowadays the same work is more conveniently achieved by using air as the material transmitting power to the brakes.

Professor A. M. Richardson of the University of Illinois has recently in a striking manner taken advantage of the mechanical properties of air to use it as a structural material. When the 'stiffness' of air was considered in a scientific manner and compared with that of other substances, it was found that it could be employed as a filling for 'pneumatic bricks'. The bricks are triangular, about three feet on each side and four inches thick. The air is packed in at a pressure of two pounds per square inch and is kept in place by an outer skin of a plastic 'such as Mylar, polyethylene or saran'. Needless to say, the pneumatic bricks, though found to be strong, are very much lighter than conventional bricks and can be used, for example, to construct very large domes. 'Entirely new possibilities in homes, schools, stores and commercial and factory buildings may be provided by the bricks,' writes the technical journal reporting Professor Richardson's project.

> *It was a miracle of rare device,*
> *A sunny pleasure-dome with caves of ice!*

But the scientific achievements in the use of air as a structural material, whether for building purposes, for the working of machinery, for supporting aeroplanes or collecting the dust off carpets, are not by any means of equal interest to those that have taken place in our understanding of the function of air for breathing.

The active constituent of air is the oxygen in it. Almost as soon as oxygen was discovered to exist at all a major advance in scientific philosophy occurred with the recognition that the snapping together of carbon and oxygen was one of the basic chemical sources of all energy on earth. Every schoolboy now knows that when you warm up a thin stick of wood hotter and hotter, suddenly a point is reached when the carbon of the wood and the oxygen of the air begin voraciously to combine together and go on doing so with so great an evolution of heat-energy that we see a flame. In 1780, Lavoisier, the first man to apply the balance and the thermometer to the investigation of the phenomenon of life, opened the modern era of the science of biological energetics. 'La vie est une fonction chimique,' he said. And he measured the amount of oxygen consumed by a man each hour and related it to the food consumed, the work done and the temperature and from this he saw that life was indeed a flame in which carbon is burned in oxygen. The carbon comes from food, the oxygen from air and the amounts of each can be measured.

Lavoisier's flash of insight was to understand that life was a burning, but slow and controlled burning compared with the abrupt and catastrophic chemistry of fire at 700° C. Food is only the half of life. Without air, with its active filling of oxygen, the combustion of the carbon in food cannot proceed.

Twenty years or so ago a number of those who had worked with Sir Frederick Gowland Hopkins at Cambridge combined together to celebrate his seventy-fifth birthday. Each of them wrote an essay touching on some aspect of the new ideas on life that this one man's ideas had in whole or in part initiated. One of his disciples, Albert von Szent-Györgyi, by then professor in the University of Szeged in Hungary, wrote about the glimmerings of a fresh conception of how air and its oxygen works in our tissues. What Szent-Györgyi wrote about as new in the fourth decade of the century can now be seen in the sixth to be only part of an elegant unity of biological mechanism extending from the tissues of man to the leaves of the pink flowering glaucus stone-crop.

Szent-Györgyi wrote that whatever a cell does has to be paid for in the currency of energy. If there is no free energy available there is no life. The animal cell does not generate its own energy. It obtains energy ready-made from outside in small parcels which are the molecules of foodstuffs. The cell knows two methods of getting the energy out of these molecules: it either fragments them or burns them.

The first method is fermentation. It is much the simpler of the two processes but at the same time it is very uneconomical since the greater part of the energy still remains undistributed. In the fermentation carried out by living yeast cells—not very active creatures—the residual energy is left unused (by the yeast) in the alcohol remaining. Similarly, the athlete who runs a hundred yards without drawing breath—as all good sprinters do—goes into 'oxygen debt' and leaves most of his fuel unburnt in the form of lactic acid.

The way fermentation works is pretty well known. The splitting of the food molecules takes place in a number of stages. The energy is released bit by bit. Phosphate in the living cells is intimately concerned in the process and works like the twisting and untwisting of rubber bands to transmit the energy as it is liberated. The process of fermentation does not require air and the oxygen it carries. There is little doubt that it is one of the older processes of life capable of maintaining only the simplest kinds of organism. The development of more complicated and pretentious forms of life became possible only after Nature discovered oxidation by molecular oxygen, brought to the living cells by the air that is the topic of discussion in this chapter. The course of events is still reflected in our own cells, in which we find oxidation and fermentation intimately mixed and woven into one combined energy-producing system. About thirty times as much energy is released by oxidation. It has been found that in order to enable us to make use of oxygen in our tissues we possess a whole group of peculiarly reactive substances in our cells each of which forms a connected series. And these enzymes, as they are termed, are brought to bear on a series of substances that form and re-form as a kind of cyclical conveyor system. The nature of these compounds only differs in a subtle way—the elegance of the chemistry can be appreciated by a chemist with the same thrill of delight felt by a sensitive reader who first reads a new poem—from the simpler substances in the fermentation system. But these differences allow the use of air, that is of its oxygen, to unlock energy for life.

'This simple conclusion', wrote Szent-Györgyi, 'gave me the greatest mental satisfaction which I have experienced in my life as a scientific worker. That is why I now offer it to Sir F. G. Hopkins. I would like to end by giving expression to my most sincere desire that oxidation and fermentation alike may long continue to interact harmoniously in the cells of our beloved teacher.'

Since 1937, when this was written, the philosophy of biochemical science has undergone yet another transformation. The respiration cycle by which energy is released had been known to include a round dozen of separate substances each differing by one chemical stage from the last. Each of these had been identified and its place in the process assured. Then, within the last five years or so it seemed as if too many substances were to be found. The mechanism that made biological life tick in air had been taken apart and put together again; but now there were several little wheels left over. Gradually, from a number of confusing observations of different types of living cells, animals, yeasts, plants, in reports coming from different universities it began to be apparent that a new system of energy-release existed, supplementary to that glimpsed by Szent-Györgyi and his contemporaries.

Among the 'unwanted' substances identified was a peculiar compound called 'sedo-heptulose'. This had been first discovered by a botanist and was isolated from the leaves of the pink flowering glaucus stone-crop. Sedo-heptulose collects in the leaves when the sun shines on them but disappears at night. Here then was a clue. Our own cells, those of an insect, a yeast cell or of a leaf all share much of the same mechanism.

In the leaves, Nature has arranged a series of enzymes that build up the simple sugars synthesised by the sun and form them eventually into the complex materials we so thoughtlessly eat. Sedo-heptulose is one of the intermediate substances in the chemical chain by which plants manufacture sugar from carbon dioxide gas. The living leaf cell possesses among all its enzymes one that gives rise to sedo-heptulose and one that takes this further into the next stage of sugar synthesis. Thus the living plant creates sugar. But when we eat it we break it down again, first by the simple systems of fermentation and then using air and the first type of respiration cycle. Latest stage of all in our evolutionary development, we use in our own bodies some of the same enzymes possessed by the plant. But whereas the green leaf uses a series of linked reactions to build up sugar, with the energy of the sun to make the process go and the strange substance, sedo-heptulose, as an intermediate stage, we—it now appears—make use of some of the same enzymes, and have in our tissues this same intermediary when we break down sugar and get the energy out of it again.

A wise man once said that all thought and philosophy was joined together in one long strand like a ball of wool, that one had only to pull steadily at one end and all ideas and knowledge would eventually be drawn out. If this be so, we might do worse for the philosophical scientist than 'give him air'.

# 12

# THE DEDICATED CELL

WHEN I was a child, forty or so years ago, and used to ask the sort of questions children do—for example, 'When a worm is cut in half, how do the separated parts know whether to grow a new head or a new tail?'—people used to tell me, 'That is one of the mysteries we are not intended to understand.' Nowadays we all know that science is wonderful and can answer every question. Or to put it more seriously, the philosophy that we of the automatic age believe is that there is no subject that cannot be examined by the scientific method with the hope that—even if some time must elapse—we may eventually expect to reach an answer.

But it is not so very long since 1905. It was in that year that Einstein came to the conclusion, solely based on *thinking*, that mass and energy might be interchangeable. This process of thought could be followed by any capable mathematician with a stump of pencil and a piece of paper. Its perhaps unnecessarily dramatic confirmation was demonstrated to the world at Hiroshima. Today we know so much about the physical structure of matter that we can either take it apart—and set up a Calder Hall—or put it together, using, say, hydrogen at Bikini or in the north-west of Australia.

'Nature and Nature's laws', wrote Alexander Pope, 'lay hid in night; God said, *Let Newton be!* and all was light.' That is to say, three hundred years ago or so, Isaac Newton fitted together the mass of unco-ordinated information then existing about physics into a logical system. Ever since, physics has been to a large degree a tidy and logically satisfying branch of science. By the end of the eighteenth century, chemistry as well was annexed to that territory of scientific knowledge over which the tidy-minded human intellect could, without excessive conceit, claim dominion. It is interesting (and perhaps encouraging as well) to notice how there were among the minds that have carried us forward into the present state of scientific enlightenment, those who were devout and religious. Einstein was, as we know, a fervent believer in peace. And in chemistry, Joseph Priestley, whose contribution to the discovery of oxygen was of major importance in the history of scientific thinking, made Birmingham too hot to hold him by reason of his perfervid Low-Church views as a clergyman. John Dalton who, so to speak, invented chemical formulae and thus rendered the manipulation of chemical ideas rational and manageable was a Quaker.

The latest branch of chemistry to achieve the status of a more or less completed set of dogma, capable of being taught to undergraduates as the accepted Truth, with a capital T, is biochemistry. This advance in the background of knowledge which forms the intellectual environment of the scientist today is new and—like Darwin's *Origin of Species* in its day—is worth construing for the ordinary non-scientist. Besides which, it forms the springboard for a discussion of cells. It is difficult for scientific people of the 1950's to put themselves into the position of their equals of the 1850's. But it is highly salutary for them to do so from time to time.

About a hundred years ago, there was no understanding of the nature of disease. All the knowledge about infection that we take in our stride today only began to be discovered in 1860 or thereabouts by Louis Pasteur. And until about the same date it was generally believed that living bodies were not composed of the same structural stuff as the other things in the world, but were compounded of a special 'vital force'. But when chemists constructed in their laboratories what had hitherto been considered to be strictly animal substances, it could be said that biochemistry had been born.

This new branch of science started in a quiet way. Chemical substances in living tissues were identified one by one. The principal components of animals and plants were gradually isolated in more and more detail. Protein, the structural substance of muscular tissue, was studied and found to be composed of a mosaic of nitrogen-containing 'amino acids'; fat-containing lipoids were investigated; and the nature and variety of carbohydrates listed and docketed. More and more substances became available for inclusion in the appropriate chapters of text-books to be learnt by successive generations of students. Sterols, complex components of certain fats, came into the picture; hormones and enzymes secreted by specialised glands such as the thyroid, the liver, the suprarenals, the pancreas, the duodenum and other parts of the digestive machinery were characterised one by one. Then came the vitamins.

As the scientific tools became sharper and better analytical techniques became available the understanding of what all these things were doing in living tissues began by fits and starts to emerge. Then, just as Newton became able to digest the facts of physics, and Darwin to unify the variety of zoology, so, in the more specialised field of biochemistry, it became possible to glimpse the ordered chemical movement that was keeping biological life going. Now that we live in a historical period when we expect a new scientific discovery to be announced every year or so it is easy to lose our sense of wonder. But it would be unimaginative in the extreme if we failed to recognise that this new *biochemical* revolution is an important milestone in human thought!

But there have been one or two peculiar setbacks in this triumphant march of resurgent biochemistry. For instance, there was the peculiar case of the cholesterol in the bile of the hippopotamus.

During the 'descriptive phase' of biochemistry the substance cholesterol was discovered in bile, the digestive juice produced by the liver. And it was gratifying to early investigators to observe that into whichever animal they looked cholesterol was to be found in its bile. But then came the check! A great 'hand-book' of physiological chemistry, as it was called, came out in which the chemical composition of the bile of a long series of beasts was reported. In all of them but one, cholesterol was duly listed. Only in the bile of the hippopotamus was it stated to be absent.

For some years, examination candidates, dredging the shallows of miscellaneous information for mark-producing pearls of wisdom, used to treasure this extraordinary omission on the part of Creation. Until, upon the timely death of a hippopotamus in the London Zoo, the matter was reinvestigated. Then, as might have been prognosticated, the cholesterol was, in verity, discovered in its bile. Apparently, the first textbook writer had, in all diligence, listed every animal about whose bile information was available and found the information—if not the cholesterol—lacking for the hippopotamus. It only required a subsequent scientific author to misphrase a single sentence for the rumour about so prominent an animal to be started on its course.

But this was just a ripple on the rising tide of biochemistry. Seventy years or so ago, Darwin and the great naturalists of the nineteenth century told us how we got here on earth. We are not, they said, angels, but merely members of the animal kingdom who owe our special powers to the processes of evolution. Today, biochemistry, with equal assurance, tells us how we work. The animation of living is not a special 'life force'. It is an explicable set of chemical reactions requiring a recognisable fuel for its operation. And, latest discovery of all, biochemistry is now proposing to explain how it is we are like we are.

Present in the nucleus of all living cells is a special compound called 'deoxyribonucleic acid'—DNA for short. (Once upon a time, chemical compounds were given 'trivial' names, like hesperidine, ionone or obtusatic acid. Now that scientific logic demands that we give them 'systematic' names, there is a gain in meaning but, unfortunately, a loss in euphony.) This stuff possesses an immense molecule, the atomic structure of which is in the form of two corkscrews twined together. Experimental evidence is gradually accruing that it is this DNA that transmits hereditary characteristics from one generation to another. At the Royal Society's Conversazione, held in London in 1956, there was a model of a molecule of DNA. It portrayed the helical coils, each consisting of at least a thousand twists and made up of links of phosphate, a rather unusual sugar, ribose, and a group of nitrogen-containing 'bases' arranged and rearranged in a sequence of 'code words', as it were. This code, we are now to suppose, spells out what kind of cells our cells are to be.

It is interesting to see the odd parallelism between the way biochemists are beginning to visualise this long, varied and twisted 'tape' of DNA and the way in which, in quite a different field of thought, physicists are today—very much in the public eye—using a not widely dissimilar arrangement. The modern electronic computer is capable of doing a long series of quite complicated things. It is, within the limits to which it is designed, capable of meeting a variety of external challenges. And it is prepared to correct its own mistakes—again within the limits of its built-in capabilities. The 'memory unit' of this machine may be a magnetic tape or drum. Such a drum is, like the DNA molecule in the living gene, a helix containing a varied pattern in code that tells a whole factory, it may be, what to do. The pattern on the 'memory' drum is laid on by disturbing the molecular arrangement magnetically. The pattern of a DNA molecule in a living cell, consisting of the order in which the molecular groups are strung together, is derived from the same pattern in the 'mother' cell from which it was derived. We might argue that if a man-made machine can already work out P.A.Y.E. and pay the wages, play a game of chess, and make motor-cars, there is no reason why such a machine should not be made able to reproduce itself. If a suitably patterned magnetic tape can enable it to do this, a suitably composed DNA molecule can make another cell like itself.

The electronic computer that is set up to do accounts, or to control the manufacture of motor-cars—or of other electronic computers—is 'programmed' by a man who has designed it to perform its purpose. But who has designed the DNA molecule, in all its elegant complexity, for its purpose? Scientists can give some sort of an answer to this question. The DNA molecule is produced by the parent cell from which it came. And this parent was in its turn the child of the evolutionary process by which living things of increasing complexity have been developed through the ages. Pursuing the matter still further, the scientist now has a hypothesis to explain the origin of biological life. This hypothesis is supported on quite reasonable evidence and some experimental observations as well. In 1952, Miller in the University of Chicago succeeded in demonstrating the synthesis of amino acids, the basic constituents of protein, from water, hydrogen, ammonia and methane in the presence of ultra-violet light. These gases and this light could be found in an uninhabited planet.

Biology, as a science, is in the middle of a vista in which the evolutionary process, which can perhaps be defined in brief as fitness for purpose, shows inorganic gases progressing forward to the most complex forms of life. In the other direction, backwards that is, the *astronomers* see the 'biology' of stars: hydrogen atoms constantly being created in the expanding universe, stars being born, living out their lives in the enormously slower time-scale of this 'astro-biology' and finally, it appears, dying— to become the dense, cold, dark bodies now known to be hanging inert in space. But with all this knowledge at hand prudent scientists are not so naïve as to believe that they are in sight of the answer to the question of how the DNA molecule became what it is.

Today the biologists know a great deal about what happens when cells become fertilised, about how they begin to develop in their early stages, and about what can be done to interfere with their development by experimental means at each stage of the growth of the creature that is developing. There is no shortage of theories either. The 'genes' in the nucleus of the cells have power to influence how those cells divide and what they become. And the chemical nature of the rest of the cells and the kind of environment in which the whole system is living exert, for their part, a reciprocal influence on what the nucleus does. Biologists know quite a lot about the geography of the single fertilised cell. 'This part of the egg', they can say, 'is going to turn into a foot and this part into a head.' And then they can add some foreign material or cut the egg about and make two legs, or two heads for that matter, grow where Nature intended there to be only one. They can define an 'individuation field' in an embryo, which is the area capable of turning into a forelimb, let us say, and nothing else. Or they can identify an 'organisation centre' which makes other tissues grafted near it turn into whatever kind of tissue the particular built-in 'organiser' may be organising, perhaps nerve cells.

But in spite of all this knowledge, biology is a science that is still in the descriptive phase. There are some biologists who think that it always will be. But this is, perhaps, unduly pessimistic. Be that as it may, in spite of what seems to be very precise and definite biochemical information, in spite of detailed knowledge of the function of phosphate in the cell as the basis of vital energy, and even now that the enormous, complex make-up of the nucleic acids that shape the chemical pattern of living has been elucidated—yet the vague biological concepts of genes, organisers and ooplasms may explain what the biologist sees just as accurately—or just as hazily, if we see it better that way—as the superficially more precise terms of biochemistry.

Newton's laws of motion, hailed so enthusiastically by Pope, were in fact a simplification of the truth. About this simplicity J. C. Squire wrote, 'It did not last; the Devil, howling *Ho!* Let *Einstein be!* restored the status quo.' The establishment of biochemistry as a science in its own right has been a remarkable development in intellectual thought. The understanding of the chemistry of how life works is a major achievement of the human mind. And the elucidation of the structure—and probably the function as well—of DNA presages great things to come. But, before we become too arrogant in our scientific successes, we still have with us some few remaining students of what used to be called natural history to tell us that biology is a science as well as chemistry. And even if we know all about one, we certainly have not begun to know all about the other. Here for us to wonder over, is a single cell irrevocably dedicated to its future. A single, fertile cell, only properly visible under the microscope. It divides, and divides and grows organs, and specialised tissues, and gets larger—all by itself in a pond, or an egg-shell, or a womb—and becomes—what? A fruit fly? An elephant? A man? And the 64,000-dollar question remains to be answered: once it has started, how does it know what to do next?

Now we have travelled a very long way towards being able to answer this question. The answer is certainly going to be a great deal more complicated than we at one time supposed. The immense size of such substances as deoxyribonucleic acid and their possibility of existing in as many permutations and combinations as a football-pool coupon makes the chance of being able to solve an individual problem somewhat remote. Nevertheless, the purpose of this chapter is to show how very far in this fundamental field of biology the scientific understanding of the facts of life has progressed. Indeed, we can take pride in the substantial advance of scientific knowledge that has been achieved. To my mind, however, the solution of material problems, even such complex ones as the nature of the built-in guidance that directs the ultimate development of a growing cell, is *not* the most important challenge to science. In my view, the top problem is how to bring the truly immense depth of scientific knowledge about Nature that our new tools and increasing experience are adding to every day into harmony with the other philosophies by which we live? Let me give an example.

In parallel with the studies of the embryological development of creatures from their original cells that we have been discussing in the last few pages, there has also been a lot of work on the factors affecting growth in animals and those that influence the ultimate ageing of the creature and its length of life. I will take one aspect of this.

In 1955 a long series of brilliant researches reached a triumphant conclusion. In a crowded lecture room in Brussels the separate researches of three groups of British chemists, of a chemical team in the United States, and of a new type of X-ray crystallography done at Oxford were seen each to support the same conclusion about the chemical configuration of vitamin $B_{12}$. The romantic chain of events had been as follows.

The disease pernicious anaemia was first shown in 1926 to be due to the lack of an active factor obtainable from liver. Hence, to keep alive, a sufferer from pernicious anaemia needed to eat nauseatingly large amounts of liver every day. Efforts were made to concentrate the active substance from liver and gradually more and more potent preparations were prepared. At last in 1948, after twenty-two years' work, the pure substance, now called vitamin $B_{12}$, was obtained. The gifted chemist who first obtained a few milligrams of it from some tons of liver succeeded where lesser men had failed because he had the simple yet common-sense acumen to notice that active preparations were always red. Consequently in carrying out successive processes of purification he always collected the red fractions, and by systematically pursuing the red colour he was finally rewarded.

The purpose of the work on vitamin $B_{12}$ was the treatment of pernicious anaemia; and this purpose was safely achieved. But within a year of the discovery it was shown that when pigs or chickens were fed on wholly vegetable diets with vitamin $B_{12}$ added their rate of growth was markedly accelerated. Now speed of growth is obviously a good thing for a farmer who, in the twentieth century, is occupied in applying the most up-to-date scientific methods to the 'manufacture' of meat. So, spurred on by the hope of glittering economic prizes, pharmaceutical manufacturers—and university research directors as well—set their scientists to work to find the most economic sources of vitamin $B_{12}$. It was soon found that a cheaper and more convenient source of the vitamin than liver was the by-product left over from the manufacture of the antibiotic drugs, streptomycin and aureomycin. But while vitamin $B_{12}$ concentrates prepared from these residues were being tested, it was quite unexpectedly discovered that the antibiotics themselves also possessed a stimulating effect on growth. Now, besides having vitamin $B_{12}$ to feed to pigs and chickens to make them grow faster, the up-to-date agriculturalist can also add penicillin, aureomycin, terramycin or bacitracin; and it can be fed not only to chickens, but to turkeys, pigs, or rats for that matter as well.

Science is an excellent and effective philosophy as long as a clear purpose, preferably some obvious material objective, is to be aimed at. As I have just said, the farmer's purpose is to manufacture bacon, pork and poultry as economically as he can. Provided, therefore, that the continuous addition of antibiotics to their food is not going to encourage the emergence of strains of pathological bacteria resistant to antibiotics that will then infect the pigs and poultry and perhaps the people who later on eat them, it is obviously to everyone's advantage to encourage their more rapid growth in this way. But having seen the effect of vitamin $B_{12}$ and antibiotic drugs on the rate of growth of animals, the scientific physiologist next extended his scope to study their effect on children. It has already been reported from the United States that the addition of vitamin $B_{12}$ to the diet of children makes them grow more quickly. Trials have been made in Great Britain and, it seems, abandoned—not because the British scientists do not *want* the children to grow quicker but because they did not find that the vitamin $B_{12}$ had any effect on making them do so.

According to the late Mr Stephen Leacock, an average Englishwoman is 5 feet $2\frac{1}{2}$ inches tall, weighs 8 stone 6 pounds, has one and three-quarters children and lives in the middle of the Bristol Channel. Be that as it may, the average Glasgow schoolgirl of nine years old was, in 1955, 4 feet 3 inches tall and weighed 4 stone 6 pounds. In 1913, when the Corporation of Glasgow first began to measure children, the little girl's average mother at nine years old was only 4 feet tall and weighed 3 stone $12\frac{1}{2}$ pounds. Now a great deal of scientific thought has been given to the problem of how to make the Glasgow schoolchildren bigger and much of the increase in the size of the little average nine-year-old girl is attributed to scientific nutrition. But although every one in the 1950's has no doubts that to be *bigger* is to be *better*, very little thought or no thought at all has been given to the reason for this belief. As I have said before, science, as currently conceived, can only deal with one thing at a time. Of course, the child is not really *bigger*. What has happened is that she has got bigger quicker. In fact, at nine years old she is physically, and probably mentally as well, identical with her grandmother at 11 years old. And now there is the new scientific information about vitamin $B_{12}$ and antibiotics that enables us to cause her to grow even faster. But for once another outcrop of new scientific knowledge has appeared that may throw an unexpected doubt into the mind of the orthodox one-problem-at-a-time scientific philosopher.

If you keep water-fleas and by restricting their food supply cause them to grow more slowly than they otherwise would they live about 40 per cent longer. Similarly, if you feed the larvae of the caterpillars of *Lymentria dispar* only every other day, they also live longer. One can pursue this principle into various parts of the zoological jungle. For example, ticks, *Dermacentor variabilis*, will live for two years or more provided that they do not get any satisfactory feeding. Once let them attach themselves to an adequate host, however, and they will over-eat and die within a few weeks.

I referred earlier to the classical experiment of Dr Clive McCay at Cornell University. He showed that if the young rats were given a balanced diet with the total amount restricted, their length of life was very greatly increased. There seems to be little doubt that the general biological evidence all leads to the conclusion that a 'high plane of nutrition' in early life merely accelerates the passing of youth and shortens the total life span. Professor McCance of Cambridge has pointed out that mothers who have been living on a 'low plane of nutrition' have babies that both anatomically and physiologically possess a biological age younger than their calendar ages. He said, as we saw, that the 'physiological age' of the bones of European children in 1946 could be increased in one calendar year by the equivalent of two years' ageing when they were given a changed diet providing unlimited calories. He commented—and the scientific evidence from many directions confirms the deduction—that the modern desire to attain the most rapid growth in children is likely to shorten their eventual span of life.

Scientific philosophy must be considered in relation to purpose. What is the purpose of acquiring knowledge of the biochemistry of the life process? What is the purpose of studying the mechanisms controlling the development of the cell? Why are we interested in researches about the rate of growth and the contribution thereto of vitamin $B_{12}$? Are we to apply our understanding of the chemistry of growth rate in order to get children to grow faster and faster even at the cost of making life shorter?

Modern orthodox science has nothing to say about purpose and is, in fact, shy and embarrassed at the very suggestion that, as an important philosophy influencing twentieth-century affairs, it should. Geriatrics, the study of long life, is now a respectable branch of modern biological science. Not long ago I attended a solemn scientific conference on ageing at which an important research worker was reporting the scientific evidence showing the circumstances in which the physical efficiency of industrial workers could be prolonged by postponing their retirement or, if they had already retired, sending them back (purely for their own good, mark you!) to their factory or mine. The reasoning and the statistics were unassailable. Their date of burial was indubitably postponed. But when the suggestion was made that perhaps Man had not been placed by God on this globe to spend his days digging in a coal-mine or screwing up nuts at a travelling belt, the scientific conference took the question and its implication as an arrant piece of bad taste. The prolongation of life is a matter of science. The purpose of the extended life has nothing to do with the case.

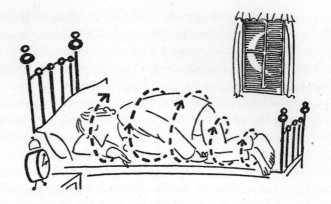

# 13

# SLEEP

SCIENCE is today applied to almost every aspect of civilised life. The effort to manufacture and export more goods, which is the principal activity of industrial civilisation, is supported by scientific endeavour applied not only to the mechanical techniques employed but also to the people using them. The art of management is nowadays a science. The health of the workers is intensively studied in relation to their productivity. The science of nutrition is harnessed to the output of industrial operatives. Housing, the provision of crèches, physical recreation, right motivation—all are co-ordinated according to the conclusions of scientific discovery.

At every point, science can claim successes. But there are fields in which scientific endeavour, in spite of the collection of a considerable mass of information, has failed to achieve any advance at all. As an example, let us take sleep.

Thirty years ago and more, the Industrial Fatigue Research Board studied the maximum number of hours of work which would give the maximum output of work by an industrial operative. Clearly, if too many hours of overtime are worked the law of diminishing returns will begin to operate and effective productivity will fall. The Industrial *Fatigue* Research Board has now become the Industrial *Health* Research Board—but the single most important factor restricting industrial output still remains: the necessity for men and women to spend approximately one-third of their time in sleep.

There are numerous theories about the cause of sleep. The first is generally attributed to Alcmeon who was a contemporary of Pythagoras in the sixth century B.C. According to him, sleep was due to the retreat of the blood into the veins. Aristotle, on the other hand, considered it to be due to what he termed 'evaporation attendant upon the process of nutrition'—hence the drowsiness occurring after meals. Some thousands of years after these views were expressed, a gentleman called Mosso, in 1880, considered that there was experimental evidence to show that sleep was due to anaemia of the brain. On the other hand, by about 1914 other investigators came to quite the opposite view and concluded that it was due to a plethora rather than a shortage of blood in the brain. In 1935, however, a report was published to show that there was no difference in the blood flow to the head in sleep and in wakefulness. We must, therefore, start to think again.

Pavlov, the great Russian physiologist, whose words are today taken as holy writ over the eastern half of the globe, considered sleep to be the result of a type of conditioned reflex. Pavlov, of course, himself developed much of our views on conditioned reflexes and it is therefore not unnatural that he should have viewed sleep from this aspect. The type of conditioned reflexes which made Pavlov most widely famous were based on experiments with dogs. The dogs were trained to associate the sound of the ringing of a bell in one corner of the room with the appearance of their dinner. A gong sounded in the other corner of the room on the other hand connoted no such attractive experience. When the animals had learned their lesson, that is to say, when they had acquired a 'conditioned reflex' in which the bell, even without the dinner, caused their gastric juices to flow, the experiment was changed. Now, the gong meant food and the bell disappointment. In due course, however, this second 'conditioned reflex' was acquired and the dogs were trained automatically to go for their dinner to the corner where the gong was. Finally, however, both bell and gong were sounded together. The dogs became torn with indecision, developed neuroses and eventually suffered nervous breakdown.

Be that as it may, Pavlov considered that sleep was due to what he called 'internal inhibition which is widely irradiated, extending over the whole mass of the cerebral hemispheres and involving the lower centres of the brain as well'. As this sample of prose suggests, Pavlov's experiments are rather difficult to interpret. They were based on the fact that dogs, put on a stand and subjected to monotonous sound, or, alternatively, kept in a soundproof room, usually fall asleep. These experiments, frequently repeated, were considered by Pavlov and his school to set up a 'conditioned reflex' in which sleep was an element.

A theory of sleep, advanced by Claparède in 1905, is that it is an 'instinct'. 'We sleep', he said, 'not because we are intoxicated or exhausted, but in order to prevent our becoming intoxicated or exhausted.' According to this thesis, sleep results from a loss of interest in one's environment, and we wake up because we become tired of sleeping.

A further postulate which has from time to time received scientific support is that sleep is due to the accumulation of some sort of toxin in the system. No research worker, however, has yet been able to give any idea of the nature of this hypothetical substance. One of the principal arguments against this theory is that Siamese twins, who share the same blood supply and who could therefore be expected to be affected equally by this alleged toxin, do not necessarily sleep at the same time. This was observed, both with the twins exhibited by Barnum and Bailey at the beginning of this century and in 1938 by Professor Speransky in a pair whom he studied in Moscow. Another reason for doubting the toxin theory is the poor performance of many people immediately after getting up in the morning, when it might be expected that such a toxin would be at its lowest concentration.

Having dealt with anaemia, conditioned reflexes, instinct and toxins, let us now turn our attention to an American investigator, Professor Kleitman. He developed an elaborate theory of sleep in an important monograph published in 1939. He suggested that it is not *sleep* that needs to be explained but *wakefulness*. And he explained wakefulness on the basis of what he called an 'evolutionary theory'.

The theory of biological evolution is nowadays a part of the general intellectual context in which we live. At the bottom of the evolutionary tree we have single-celled organisms such as amoebae, then come the sort of creatures one sees through a microscope in a drop of pond water, and so we go on via fishes and frogs until we reach the anthropoid apes and, at last, as the finest flower on the topmost bough, we find ourselves, *Homo sapiens*. Side by side with the theory of evolution, there is the theory of recapitulation. This is nowadays somewhat discredited by modern biologists but it nevertheless possesses certain points of interest. It implies that each individual man himself undergoes the entire system of evolution. When a man is conceived he exists first as a single-celled organism. This organism multiplies and develops until it passes through the successive stages of fish, frog and ape before being born as an infant man. Kleitman in his theory of sleep implies that the great fraction of biological creation which includes what we call the lower organisms cannot be said to be awake at all. Even so advanced a creature as a baby, which, if we accept the theory of recapitulation, we could consider to be near, if not at, the apex of the evolutionary tree, spends most of its time asleep.

As with all theories of sleep, that of Kleitman is not completely convincing. For example, whether or not we agree with Swift as to the relative positions of horses and men in biological advancement, the amount of sleep they each take hardly supports Kleitman's hypothesis. If men were higher up the biological tree than horses they ought to sleep less, but they do not. There is, however, a curious phenomenon which does support Kleitman's 'evolutionary' theory of sleep and wakefulness.

If you scratch the sole of the foot of a healthy, sleeping man he will bend his big toe back. This is called a 'positive Babinski' sign. If you scratch the sole of the foot of an orang-outang, he will bend his big toe down, which is called a 'negative Babinski' sign. Now if you deal similarly with a sleeping infant, when he is very young he will give a 'negative Babinski' sign like an anthropoid ape but as he grows older, and presumably passes from a lower to a higher evolutionary level, his Babinski sign becomes positive. Side by side with this evidence of advancing status there is the diminution of the need for sleep and an increased capacity for wakefulness.

The desire for a hypothesis to unify the groups of observations which he makes on the world's happenings is a universal craving of man. And scientists, who attempt to deal objectively with the facts which they observe, have a special intellectual need for working hypotheses. Nevertheless, although correct hypotheses are more valuable than mistaken ones, the history of science is littered with incorrect theories some of which have been found useful. For example, thirty years ago the empty spaces of the universe were filled with a hypothetical elastic fluid called aether which has since disappeared from the text-books of physics without leaving a trace. Nevertheless, in its time aether was a useful intellectual lubricant which guided the direction of a lot of profitable experimentation. It is, therefore, worth considering what constructive experimental observations have been made on sleep, even though twenty-six centuries of postulated hypothesis have failed to produce a satisfactory scientific explanation for its existence.

Some fascinating investigations have been carried out into the manner in which people move about when they are asleep. Omitting certain classical studies which could hardly

claim to have been done for scientific purposes, we come to
the observations of the American research workers who in
1927 re-designed a technique for studying sleepers previously
worked out in Germany. In principle, scientific methods are
often delightfully simple, and the way the measurements of
people's activity while sleeping were done was as follows. A
string was attached to the bedspring and was connected to a
clockwork instrument similar to the seismograph used for
recording earthquakes. This apparatus having been set up,
the scientists got to work.

First of all, 15,000 records were made of the sleeping
behaviour of eleven people who were sufficiently public-
spirited to submit themselves to examination. From all this,
the investigators calculated that the average length of time
during which a sleeping person remained without moving was
only 11·5 minutes. When they had, by this thorough if
laborious means, obtained this fact for the record they proceeded to the next stage of the research. For this they collected
a group of ninety people whom they described as 'representa-
tive groups of healthy sleepers'. And from this party of volunteers they come to the following conclusions. Middle-aged
men, they found, kept still while asleep for an average of 9
minutes; the wives of middle-aged men for 10·5 minutes; and
'unselected college men' for 12·8 minutes. That is to say, the
middle-aged men had 53 periods of movement during a
night's sleep of eight hours' duration, the wives 46 and the
students 38.

Kleitman, the distinguished American investigator whose
name I have already mentioned, designed a most complicated
and sensitive apparatus for recording automatically the movements of sleepers. By means of this he deduced that, although
people move about a good deal when they are asleep, and
move increasingly as the night passes, nevertheless they only
spend 3 to 5 minutes in making their 40 or 50 nightly movements. Another American scientist, Giddings, invented a
different type of instrument which he called a 'hypnograph'.

This was used to measure the activities of twenty-eight sleeping children. His discovery was that the amount of movement increased during each successive hour of sleep. He also found that girls slept sounder than boys. One final American research worker, with a taste for mixed classical nomenclature, invented yet another scientific instrument which on this occasion was called a 'somnokinetograph'. With this machine he discovered that the average sleeping person moves from 10 to 12 times an hour. He also found that people move in their sleep more and more often as the night goes on. To this phenomenon he gave the technical name of 'crescendo sleep'.

It is not enough for one scientist to find out that people move when they are sleeping, and another to count how often they move. This merely stimulates other researchers to go more deeply into the business and try to find out what kind of movements sleepers make and some of the factors which increase or decrease the activity of the movements they undertake. In 1932, a group of scientists came out with the discovery that 'certain types of moving pictures' led to disturbed sleep and 'increased motility' in children. They also discovered that other moving pictures had what they described as 'a sedative effect'. This effect is occasionally observed by non-scientific people who have exposed themselves unwittingly to the wrong type of film.

Apart from studies of the ordinary sorts of movements that we all apparently perform while asleep a number of special kinds of movement have been investigated during the course of sleep research. An Italian investigator called Masci published a learned paper about a young man who rolled his head from side to side 75 times a minute while he was asleep. A French savant, Bertoye, also observed this phenomenon—which he dignified as *jactatio capitis nocturna*—in a child. In both cases, the scientists were unable to stop the head-rolling; it should perhaps be said that the victims slept perfectly well in spite of their activities.

I should like to turn now from discussing all these diligent scientific studies that have been made into how people move about while they are asleep to the equally serious researches that have been made into how soundly people sleep. The first of the modern investigators was probably Kohlschutter who, in 1862, determined how hard he needed to hit a slate slab with a hammer in order to wake a sleeper at different times of the night. The results obtained by this somewhat primitive technique are today considered to be suspect. What we must, I suppose, consider to be a more refined and scientific method was used in 1930 by two other German workers, Endres and Von Frey, who calculated the depth of sleep by measuring the force required to wake a person by prodding him with a bristle. Kleitman and his colleagues in America, on the other hand, measured the voltage required to produce sufficient noise from a loud-speaker to wake the sleepers they were studying.

And what was the result of all this?

It was found that when a person was moving in bed he was very easily wakened. During a period of stillness, the depth of sleep increased continuously up to a point shortly before the next movement was due to occur, and then it fell to a low value when the person was actually moving. Since people move less frequently at the beginning of a night's sleep, they also tend to sleep most deeply early in the night. As a general rule, we sleep less deeply as the night passes and we move about more and more frequently. Sometimes, contrary to the general trend, one, or perhaps two, periods of comparatively deeper sleep may occur during the latter half of the night.

Scientific research, no matter towards what object it is aimed, always follows the same general strategy. First, a general view of what is to be studied. In the case of sleep, some approximate observations on the unconsciousness occurring during sleep, the time occupied in sleep and the look of people asleep. Then comes the construction of a hypothesis, anaemia of the brain, let us say. It is then examined and found to be wrong. What of the other hypotheses, that sleep is a habit? A reflex? Evolutionary? To check each, more facts are required and must be collected. But while this is being done, there is no reason why we should not assume that one of the explanations for sleep may not be right. If it is, we can look at the way sleep fits into the rhythm of daily life and then use our discoveries about sleep and its cause to change this daily rhythm—that is, if our conclusions on the subject are right.

It has been known for at least a hundred years that there is a more or less regular day and night variation in a person's body temperature. One's temperature is low first thing in the morning, rises to a maximum during the day and sinks down towards bed-time, reaching a minimum at three or four o'clock in the morning. This is why life seems at its lowest at this time. This rhythm is closely related to sleep. When a man's body temperature falls below a certain point in the evening, he goes to sleep; when it exceeds a certain point in the morning, he wakes up. Kleitman and one of his collaborators, however, carried the matter to a much more subtle conclusion. They persuaded six people to undergo a series of tests. They had to deal three packs of cards into four hands, copy a 400-letter nonsense word, multiply two 8-digit numbers, and stand with their eyes closed on an instrument which recorded every time they wobbled. Kleitman and his assistant persuaded their examinees to do these tests five times a day—immediately they got up in the morning, one hour later, immediately before lunch, just before their evening meal, and at bed-time. When the results of the tests were examined it was found that the freedom from mistakes and the speed with which the tests were done were closely proportional to the rise and fall in temperature. The importance of this observation is that temperature rhythms vary from one individual to another. Some people attain their highest body temperature and their greatest efficiency early in the waking period of the day, others are at their peak late. The fact that some people do their best intellectual work in the morning and others in the evening is therefore, it would seem, based on this physiological idiosyncrasy.

Nowadays, when the whole future career of a child may be decided at eleven years old by his performance at an intelligence test carried out on a single day, it would be reasonable to arrange also to take his temperature three or four times beforehand in order to give him the test when his temperature is highest and avoid providing an unfair advantage to the child whose physiological rhythm happens to coincide with the education authority's time-table.

The existence of this twenty-four-hour rhythm of high and low temperature can be seen to imply that seven times a week, and notably when one is asleep, one's effectiveness as a social unit is reduced. Professor Kleitman and his colleagues took up this point as something capable of experimental study. They therefore designed a series of trials to see whether the normal rhythm of high and low temperature could be changed and the incidence of trough periods reduced. The investigation was done in Mammoth Cave, Kentucky, where it is always completely dark, completely quiet and where the temperature never varies. In this environment Professor Kleitman and one companion began to live a life in which each so-called 'day' consisted of twenty-eight hours. To the world outside, their meal times and work times and bed times were four hours late each day. To them, however, all that had happened was that they had reduced the number of 'days' in a week from seven to six. Under this regime, the companion found that his physiological rhythm of body temperature, mental efficiency and sleep soon changed and fitted into the new circumstances. Professor Kleitman, on the other hand, was physiologically unable to conform and in consequence lived a very uncomfortable life during those times when his rhythm was out of step with the inverted part of one of the twenty-eight-hour days. He still had seven periods of reduced temperature a week whereas his fellow cave-mate now only had six.

All sorts of other researches have been carried out on sleep besides those that we have touched on in this chapter. Even so the scientific expert is not yet possessed of sufficient knowledge to enable him to make any practical recommendation as to how the time now spent unproductively in sleep can be reduced. Almost the only practical step which science could immediately propose would be to sort out those individuals whose rhythms are the more readily capable of being changed and to use only these for night-shift work or watch-keeping in ships. The rest of us can take comfort from the sensitive mimosa which continues to fold and unfold its leaves by night and day long after it has been removed from the sunshine into a greenhouse where the artificial light is on all the time.

This then is an account, albeit a brief and superficial one, of a long-continued research in progress. Perhaps from time to time it is salutary to recall that occasionally scientists turn on their battery of tools, apply their methods of systematic study and experimentation and, after all, do not succeed in making progress. We are nowadays so surrounded with the ostentatious triumphs of science that the possibility of anything less than success is almost forgotten. The plastic motor-cars, the colour television sets, the garage doors that open by themselves, the aeroplanes that fly faster than sound and the poliomyelitis vaccines appear so slickly one after the other that it sometimes seems that anything we want can be got merely by telling the scientist to produce it. In truth, however, discovery is not to be had for the asking. It is not very difficult to find out how many times an average forty-two-year-old bachelor moves in his sleep, nor is it a matter of great intellectual skill to measure the exact degree of ripeness at which a field of hay supplies the maximum yield of digestible fodder when given to milking cows, but it is very difficult to solve the problem of what sleep is, just as it is to elucidate the scientific causes of ageing, whether of a stalk of grass or of a human brain cell.

There are two kinds of scientific achievement. There is honest donkey work by which thousands of scientists earn their living; for example, the carrying out of statistically designed trials to determine the appropriate temperature required to obtain the maximum yield of penicillin in the fermentation vessel of a penicillin factory. And then there is the flash of intuition by which science itself is advanced—the original sudden conception that a Penicillium mould might produce a drug capable of controlling infection in human tissues.

Science is one of our modern religions. It is by definition Good. It is capable of achieving all things. It is only necessary to train more scientists to obtain more Good. Once upon a time I proposed to the broadcasting authorities a series of talks entitled 'The Failures of Science'. The idea was instantly turned down—and rightly so. It was heresy.

# 14

# FEELING FOR SCIENCE

'ONE of the most remarkable characteristics of the age in which we live is its desire and tendency to connect itself organically with preceding ages—to ascertain how the state of things that now is came to be what it is. And the more earnestly and profoundly this problem is studied, the more clearly comes into view the vast and varied debt which the world of today owes to that foreworld, in which man by skill, valour and well-directed strength first replenished and subdued the earth. Our prehistoric fathers may have been savages, but they were clever and observant ones. They founded agriculture by the discovery and development of seeds whose origin is now un-known. They tamed and harnessed their animal antagonists and sent them down to us as ministers instead of rivals in the fight for life. Later on, when the claims of luxury added them-selves to those of necessity, we find the same spirit of invention at work.'

'There are persons born with the power of interpreting natural facts, as there are others smitten with everlasting in-competence in regard to such interpretation.'

'We have been scourged by invisible thongs [the reference is to bacterial infection], attacked from impenetrable ambuscades, and it is only today that the light of science is being let in upon the murderous dominion of our foes. Facts like these excite in me the thought that the rule and governance of this universe are different from what we in our youth supposed them to be—that the inscrutable Power, at once terrible and beneficent, in whom we live and move and have our being and our end, is to be propitiated by means different from those usually resorted to. The first requisite towards such propitiation is *knowledge*; the second *action*, shaped and illuminated by that knowledge. Of knowledge we already see the dawn, which will open out by-and-by to perfect day; while the action which is to follow has its unfailing source and stimulus in the moral and emotional nature of man—in his desire for personal well-being, in his sense of duty, in his compassionate sympathy with the sufferings of his fellow men.'

To my mind the three passages above say some important things about science. Throughout this book I have been trying to grapple with some of the things which modern science has achieved. Here and there, I have pointed out some things in which it has failed. And from time to time I have attempted to describe how the materialistic philosophy science has come to be fits in with other philosophies that are of importance in civilised life.

The sentences I have quoted were written just over eighty years ago by an English physicist, John Tyndall, who himself made important contributions to the study of the role of micro-organisms in disease. They are taken from a lecture in which he reviewed the significance of the then new conclusions of the French chemist, Louis Pasteur. This discourse was delivered before the Glasgow Science Lectures Association on October 19th, 1876. The lapse of time gives somewhat piquant point to the thoughts then expressed. The first of these—that is, the dependence of present discoveries on past knowledge— is today, as it was in 1876, an essential feature of science. It is indeed one of the basic features of the modern age of discovery. What is known can be used as a basis for what next becomes known. Trade secrets handed down by word of mouth are unlikely to lead to any improvement. Interesting observations made by one craftsman will be forgotten if they are not immediately suited to current circumstances and will need to be rediscovered all over again a generation later when circumstances arise into which they would have fitted. Even today there are industries bedevilled by 'experts', who come and look, consider and give advice. This advice may be sound or it may not, but so long as the evidence upon which it is made is not disclosed it is, so far as progressive usefulness is concerned, sterile. More important still, the written and accessible record of the past has a fertilising influence on the many diverse minds of the present. Men who are working on the same problem from different standpoints may get from the scientific 'literature' the one illuminating fact that will spark off that flash of intuition that is the essential feature of the act of discovery.

There is urgent warning in this for twentieth-century science. Trade secrets when they become known are almost always seen to have been not worth knowing. Usually they have stultified the secret traders more than those supposedly kept in the dark. It arises from this that constant vigilance must be maintained in the cause of the maximum freedom of the mind in every country where knowledge of the atomic geography of the structure of matter is considered to be of military significance.

Science is a dynamic philosophy. Just as we are the product of all that has gone before in the past, so we scientific people build the discoveries of the future on the knowledge of the present. But to make progress in new building we need a measure of intellectual brilliance. Nowadays in the mid-twentieth century Tyndall's trenchant comment about those people 'smitten with everlasting incompetence'—however true it may be—has a remarkably rumbustious and undiplomatic ring.

We now know that the 'man in the street', and even more

particularly the 'politician in the House', is not interested in science for what it is. Few people even among those who consider themselves to be educated care for science as a pursuit of the truth about Nature. To the ordinary citizen, it is merely a way of doing practical things or of making economically important goods suitable to be exports for hard cash. The urgent and clamorous search for more and more scientists by the industrialists of Europe, America and Russia is not a search for people who can consider and think, but for those who manufacture. This is perhaps a fortunate thing because the problem of training this kind of 'scientist' is primarily one of administration. During a war, governments find little difficulty in training large numbers of men and women to work artillery predictors, or to plot the course of aeroplanes, to correct all the fifty-seven faults likely to arise in firing the Bren gun, or to learn the practical elements of navigation. These topics can be taught to almost anyone, whether he has previously been employed as a literary critic, a bus conductor or a professor of Old Testament history. There ought, therefore, to be equally little difficulty in teaching the same diversity of people to carry out routine chemical analysis, operate quadruple-effect evaporators or make replicate trials to test the toughness of a new plastic floor covering. There are, however, three kinds of deficiency in a community such as that in Britain straining towards 'scientific' progress; they are not capable of being solved by administrative action. The first is *understanding* by those who control industry and national administration of what scientific methods can achieve. The second is *willingness* by these people to abandon tried and customary ways and readiness to adopt the conclusions emerging from scientific study. The third deficiency is by far the most severe, as it always has been. It is, of course, a deficiency of an adequate supply of 'those persons born with the power of interpreting natural facts', to use the words of Tyndall.

The late Sir Edward Mellanby, sometime Secretary of the Medical Research Council, was an angry person. He possessed the great distinction of being the rudest man in the public service, when he felt like it. But even though burdened by the administrative cares of a great Department he managed to achieve some distinguished scientific discoveries. And he also said some true and trenchant things. One of these was that new scientific discoveries were not made because some Government committee decided that they should be, and voted funds. The big new discoveries are made by this mysterious spark of intuition given to the few prepared and dedicated intellects. For instance, we should like to find a cure for cancer, and many worthy people have given money for that purpose. We should like also to be able to prevent catching cold, and at Salisbury devoted volunteers have spent an aggregate of thousands of fortnights isolated in pairs so that various vaccines and extracts could be tried on them. And progress up to now has been restricted to finding a way to give a cold to a raw egg! The discoveries have not been made, because the insight has not been vouchsafed to those working on the problems.

But Tyndall's third passage of eighty years ago is of greatest importance to us today. It is right and proper that scientists, immersed in the intellectual intricacies of their immediate problems, should think of nothing else. The X-ray crystallographer, unravelling the complex structure of the carbon atoms arranged in porphyrin configuration around a single atom of cobalt in the molecule of vitamin $B_{12}$, must concentrate all the force of her mind (the research in question was, in fact, led by a brilliant woman, Mrs Dorothy Hodgkin, F.R.S.) on the problem in hand. And many a lesser worker must argue and struggle with details of chemical double bonds and solubilities and melting points. But nevertheless something is surely wrong with scientific professionalism if its activities are untranslatable into the plain speech comprehensible by the non-scientific educated man. And worst of all, if any mention of Divine purpose in a scientific meeting is considered in bad taste.

Today, no one of Tyndall's scientific stature would refer to a modern discovery as having modified his views 'of the rule and governance of the inscrutable Power, at once terrible and beneficent, in whom we live and move and have our being and our end'. It is a curious paradox that although science in the twentieth century in its practical manifestations affects our lives with unique directness—here as a domestic deep-freeze, there as a hydrogen bomb—it has become incapable of stirring our feelings. We view science as a tool. A spade or a typewriter or an aeroplane is merely a *thing*. We neglect the fact that science itself is a way to the truth.

Not long ago, Mr Eric Deuchars wrote a letter to *The Times* in which he deplored the action of a school headmaster, a scientist, in restricting the teaching of English and history to sixth-form boys. 'The scientist', he wrote, 'needs precision and clarity for communicating his objective knowledge of truth about the physical world; but perhaps more than ordinary men he needs to understand what artists and philosophers are trying to communicate about their search for truth in language which, being subjective and poetic will often require skill and experience for its understanding.'

In 1951, a meeting of a learned scientific society took place at Aberdeen University. A series of papers was discussed covering such topics as 'The influence of ammoniacal nitrogen on the protein content of grass-land herbage', 'The relative body dimensions of Cheviot ewes raised under range conditions and by indoor feeding methods', and 'The incidence of symptoms of central-nervous-system dysfunction in human subjects subsisting on a Vegan diet'. The 'Vegan', it should be explained, is an extreme vegetarian sect, whose members refuse to eat milk and eggs as well as meat. The general title of the meeting—somewhat fanciful in comparison with customary scientific usage—was 'All flesh is grass'. At the end of the official proceedings a reception had been arranged for the assembled chemists, physiologists and biochemists in one of the ancient halls of the University. There, one of the Fellows of the College, a non-scientist, handed to the Secretary of the meeting, as a matter of general interest to the company, an

ancient Bible and begged him to read from it. The passage was
of course from Isaiah. 'The voice said, Cry. And he said,
What shall I cry? All flesh is grass and all the goodness thereof
is as the flower of the field. The grass withereth, the flower
fadeth; because the spirit of the Lord bloweth upon it, surely
the people is grass. The grass withereth, the flower fadeth; but
the word of our God shall stand for ever.'

Having got so far, the Secretary was overcome with em-
barrassment. His voice dropped and he refused to proceed
further. The scientists, after a slight hesitant pause, resumed
their interrupted conversations. No one could bear to continue reading to the subsequent verse where the poet had said:
'Who hath measured the waters in the hollow of his hand,
and meted out heaven with the span, and comprehended the
dust of the earth in a measure, and weighed the mountains in
scales, and the hills in a balance? Who hath directed the Spirit
of the Lord, or being his counsellor hath taught him? . . . Have
ye not known? Have ye not heard? Hath it not been told you
from the beginning? Have ye not understood from the foun-
dations of the earth?'

In 1876, John Tyndall, reviewing Pasteur's studies of
fermentation and their subsequent application to medicine and
surgery, could apprehend their scientific and intellectual elegance and at the same time feel that facts like these showed that
the inscrutable Power governing the universe was to be propitiated by knowledge and by action illuminated by that knowledge. The way John Tyndall felt in 1876 is eighty years or
more past. His kind of reaction to scientific discovery has
evaporated from the mid-twentieth-century present. Much of
scientific thinking and almost all of scientific doing are performed in a philosophical vacuum today.

We cannot expect that in the future we shall ever come again
to relate the understanding of the workings of Nature as re-
vealed by scientific discovery to the purpose of the universe
in exactly the same way that John Tyndall did. Nevertheless,
there are some good auguries for a more sane philosophy in

the future than the sterile scientific materialism of the present. The first optimistic sign, in my opinion, is the spread of chemistry, up to now one of the most materialistic of the sciences, into the realm of biology. In the strictly 'chemical' fields of chemistry, the scientists might be deceived into thinking that there are no limits to the possibilities of discovery. The scope of chemical syntheses continually extends. A new substance has only to be isolated for it to be merely a matter of time and diligence before it is made artificially in the laboratory. The specification for a solvent or a textile fibre needs only to be drawn up for the chemist to be able to set to work to meet it. New paints and plastics, weed-killers and 'wonder' drugs follow each other in constant succession. But in the science of biology there is no room for workers lacking in the healthy humility that is the beginning of wisdom.

The further scientific biology advances and the more biochemistry becomes used to interpreting the phenomena of living cells, the more closely will the topics studied progress away from the investigation of individual details of the mechanism of cells and towards a consideration of the activities of the whole animal. And as the scientific biologist advances along this path, so will he progress step by step upwards from his sea-urchin's egg, and his frog, and his albino rat until he is able to tackle the reactions of man. And when he, and the chemist and physicist who now work with him, come to man as a serious topic for study, their sciences will evolve into humanities.

If this possibility of success in scientific progress is one of the great hopes for science becoming a satisfactory philosophy for the future, another of its powerful attractions for the human mind is the depth and complexity of the ultimate problems it sets. For instance, no matter how successful the practitioners of scientific medicine and surgery, the pathologists, the endocrinologists, the bacteriologists, the haematologists, the oto-rhino-laryngologists, the paediatricians and the gerontologists may be, in the end people are bound to die of *something*! A hundred years ago, the birth of bacteriology saw the conquest of infectious diseases begin. Fifty years ago, the newer knowledge of nutrition heralded the end of deficiency diseases—or, at least, it provided the information that made them preventable. The advent of the sulpha-drugs displaced pneumonia as a killing disease. The production of antibiotics radically changed the lethal nature of a dozen more of the scourges of mankind. It is only a matter of time before the virus diseases are brought under control like the bacterial infections before them. And yet people still die.

Not long ago, Dr Alex Comfort, of the Department of Zoology of University College, London, delivered a learned lecture to the Royal Institution in which he reviewed the scientific knowledge about ageing. The cumulative impact of all the information had a salutary lesson for those people who tend to assume that science can do anything. Like the researches on sleep discussed earlier, those on ageing represent one more in the 'failures of science' series. For instance longevity, it appears, tends to run in families. But science can hardly take any credit for this. Or again, smallish parts of an animal or a man can be cut off when he is young, stored carefully under refrigerated conditions or preserved as a 'tissue culture' and later grafted back on to the same man or animal when he is old. He would then be an old man with certain young parts. There seems, however, to be no possibility as yet of ever restoring to him enough of his lost youth to make much real difference to his old age. At present, there is no graft, hormone or preparation known which is capable of producing more than a limited reversal of a very few senile changes in human beings.

The only way in which biologists have been able to postpone death by scientific means has been by slowing down the rate of development in youth. I have already referred to the accelerating effect of the present 'high plane of nutrition' which we adopt so enthusiastically for children today and by which we shorten their life span. Dr Comfort points out that besides using limitation of diet in youth as a means of prolonging life it might be theoretically possible—judging by results on animals—to prolong life also by cold storage. He comments, however, that though this is now within the bounds of possibility and might be important for astronauts or perhaps politicians, it would be unlikely to be generally popular.

It was once widely believed that with the removal of 'pathological' causes of death—that is to say when medical science had at last been completely successful in all its endeavours—the life span would rise very rapidly in man and approach more and more closely the recorded maximum of about one hundred and twenty years. But it now seems more likely that even with increased control over malignant tumours, hardening of the arteries and high blood-pressure, the age of death may only come to be more and more normally distributed about seventy-five or eighty years. Nowadays, in spite of all the new scientific knowledge that is available to doctors to prolong life, it is common to find that the disease that actually kills an aged patient is only one of several; and if the patient had survived the first, one or other of the rest would soon have proved fatal.

The medical sciences have achieved great things. 'How often', says Dr William Budd in his celebrated work on typhoid fever, '—how often have I seen in past days, in the single narrow chamber of the day-labourer's cottage the father in his coffin, the mother in the sickbed in muttering delirium, and nothing to relieve the desolation of the children but the devotion of some poor neighbour, who in too many cases paid the penalty of her kindness in becoming herself the victim of the same disorder.'

The scientific philosophy that we have been discussing in this book, the logical collection of facts, the deduction of hypotheses from those facts, the design of experiments and—oh joy and delight for the scientist!—the triumphant elation when the experiments 'come out right' and demonstrate the correctness of the hypothesis, is indeed a philosophy that a civilised man can live by. Being in the main the day-to-day creatures that we are, we can enjoy the power that scientific understanding gives us and the intellectual happiness of making discoveries. And without humbug we can also share a little of the pride for having relegated the lurid picture painted by Dr Budd to the status of a period piece. It is not altogether pompous to want to benefit mankind.

But the application of scientific thinking to the material fabric of our lives does not of itself bring happiness. According to a recent estimate, six million people in the United States— that is 5 per cent of the population—are consuming eight million doses of meprobamate (a so-called 'tranquilliser') each month. And meprobamate is not alone. Since tranquillising drugs were introduced in 1954, at least four have been launched on the public. Besides meprobamate, there are chlorpromazine, reserpine and lysergic acid. And lysergic acid (innocently nicknamed by the Americans LSD) produces hallucinations as well as tranquillity! The sales of these drugs are running at about seventy-five million dollars a year. With the almost certain invention of new tranquillisers, this sum is expected to grow larger and larger.

The technical achievement of the pharmacologists who developed these novel chemical substances is one more example of the speed with which scientific research moves forward from one success to the next. But it is merely what we have come to expect. The first aeroplane to fly at 400 miles an hour was a scientific wonder—for a while. Soon we knew, however, that the sound barrier at 700 odd miles an hour would be surpassed and no one was particularly surprised when it was. Now the speed is well over 1,000 an hour, and so it goes on. But while the scientific success of producing a drug apparently combining the advantages of alcohol, caffein and aspirin with none of their disadvantages is very creditable, the important fact, to my mind, is something different. It is that so many people should want to consume these 'happiness pills' in the enormous quantities that it appears they do.

In our modern world today, science and the scientific philosophy are applied to almost every aspect of life. Chemical knowledge is used in the production and harvesting of food. The application of artificial fertilisers increases crop yields, selective weed-killers keep the fields free from unwanted plant species, and new chemical fungicides and insecticides destroy disease and insect pests. Scientific methods are applied to food storage and processing. Even the choice of the diet we eventually eat is based on calculations of vitamins, protein and calorific content. Wool, cotton and flax are no longer sufficient for our clothing and so we go to science for nylon stockings, terylene shirts and plastic mackintoshes.

The motive force that keeps our whole modern society going is a product of science. The word 'horsepower' is just a romantic anachronism to remind us of past history. The power we use, dependent on the knowledge of electricity acquired during the last eighty years, is not even any longer derived from coal. Today, we are getting it from our new scientific understanding of the basic structure of the atom itself. Even the control of our complex scientific economy, it seems, is to be done in the near future without the need for much human effort: 'Automation', the management of quite complex factory operation by electronic computers and other scientific devices, is already being applied on an increasing scale.

This is scientific progress. This kind of thing is the source of our economic wealth. Without an adequate supply of scientists and technicians we cannot enjoy a standard of living capable of giving us television sets and bicycles, ball-point pens, motor-cars fitted with automatic gear-change, jet planes and atomic power stations.

We have become so accustomed to living in a predominantly scientific environment that we tend to forget that for most of us science is only a means to an end. The comparatively few research workers who make the basic discoveries of the facts and workings of Nature follow science as a pursuit of truth, but for the rest of us it is simply the source of our material supplies and comforts.

The extraordinary enthusiasm for 'tranquillising' drugs shown by the inhabitants of New York City and Hollywood, where scientific living has probably reached a higher level than anywhere else in the world, makes one stop for a moment to think about where our science is leading us. 'I can't make up my mind whether to take a benzedrine tablet and go to a party or take a sleeping pill and go to bed,' is what the 'bright young thing' in the *New Yorker* was saying a year or two ago. Now it is reported that a synthetic martini composed of gin and meprobamate is all the rage. This beverage is designed to stimulate and to tranquillise at one and the same time.

Why do people take these drugs? You would imagine that as the scientific amenities of civilisation continuously increased and we all presumably become happier—we should be content to see life with our unaided senses. But we know that civilised life, as it insidiously mounts up around us, is not altogether easy to live. So it is interesting to listen to what Mr Luis Munos Marin, the Governor of the new commonwealth of Porto Rico, had to say about science and tranquillity when he received an honorary degree from Harvard University some months ago.

The first duty of any modern State is what Mr Marin called 'Operation Bootstrap'. This is to pull the country up by its own shoelaces; to develop new industries, produce millions of kilowatt-hours of new electric power, build efficient airports, good roads and harbours, and develop better systems of marketing. In fact, 'Operation Bootstrap' is the utilisation of applied science in just the way we are going about it in Britain. By science we can raise our standards of living, and as the standards rise and we become richer, the fight against poverty approaches closer to its ultimate success. But Mr Marin has another target in view. 'It is a basic duty', said he, 'to fight poverty. Priority obviously goes to fighting the old-fashioned poverty that consists of vast masses of people being ill-fed, ill-housed, ill-clad, ignorant, insecure in illness, orphanhood and old age. . . . . There is room also', he went on, 'for an awareness of a new-fangled poverty, that of the feverish desires outstripping the feverish production and of the feverish production inventing new desires that must go for many unfulfilled.' He called the campaign against this sort of poverty 'Operation Serenity'.

Mr Marin's approach to serenity is different from anything requiring the use of 'tranquillising' drugs. He looks forward, as we do, to the highest development of modern scientific machinery, but from Porto Rico his prospect seems somehow different. 'We Westerners tend to pursue happiness by increasing possessions,' he said to his American audience at Harvard University. 'An unending way if it is viewed as a progression from the no-house family to the three-car family and beyond.'

Clearly, the road to this three-car millennium and beyond leads also to the tranquillity of the new 'tranquillisers'. It is, therefore, interesting to look a little more closely at what they do.

Their primary use is, of course, for the treatment of psychotic patients in mental hospitals. Clearly if, under proper medical control, they can relieve sufferers from some of the more agonising aspects of mental disease, they are to be welcomed. And good results have been reported with them. On the other hand there are some people, it seems, for whom these drugs are either too good or too bad. For example, out of 8,000 odd patients given tranquillisers at the University of Oregon's Medical School, 80 became so depressed that they attempted to commit suicide, while another 126 became so happy that they neglected to take proper care of the diseases from which they were suffering and consequently became worse.

These exceptional cases at both ends of the scale demonstrate, not only how difficult it is to relate a particular chemical molecule in the form of a drug to people's mental state, but they also demonstrate the differences in behaviour occurring among different individuals. An extreme example of this is shown by the scientific assessment of the effect produced on certain people by dummy tablets not containing any drug at all. This is called the 'morale factor'.

The public interest in the new 'tranquillisers' is good in so far as it has directed attention to the relationship between chemistry and the behaviour of the mind. The Ford Foundation in the United States, to name one agency only, is already sponsoring an investigation into the possible biochemical basis of mental and emotional diseases. And there are a number of research workers studying the suggestion that a 'twisted thought' may be due to a 'twisted molecule'.

The first approach of the cold clear logic of the research scientist is always startling to the ordinary layman. For example, people are sometimes shocked to overhear the professional gusto with which one clinician will talk to another about a 'really lovely case' of chiropompholyx, or idiopathic hypocalcaemia, or whatever it may be. 'My dear old boy, an absolutely typical case! Every symptom as clear as a bell!' And then there are the experts studying the influenza virus, whose greatest success to date is to *give* influenza to a ferret.

The same thing has happened in the researches on 'tranquillisers'. Meprobamate has been tried on Siamese fighting fish. Results have been highly gratifying. When these fish are given a dose of the 'tranquilliser' they stop fighting and start swimming backwards. The effect on guppies, however, is not so calming. These fish can be made to swim backward when they are given LSD, but when they receive a dose of reserpine as well they stop swimming backwards. Research workers who have used ducklings as their laboratory animals have also made some peculiar observations. Under normal circumstances, mallard ducklings learn to follow their mothers when they are twelve hours old. If they are given a dose of the 'tranquilliser' meprobamate, however, this admirable 'mother fixation' fails to develop.

The use of social drugs by civilised societies is of long

standing. Tea, from which we obtain our daily dose off caffeine, dates back at least to the first century A.D. Alcohol has been in vogue since the time of Father Noah. Nicotine has been used in European countries since the sixteenth century. And in our own time aspirin and the barbiturate sleeping drugs have become commonplace. But there is, perhaps, something approaching the sombre prophecies of Aldous Huxley's *Brave New World* in the thought of large numbers of people having to steel themselves to face the tension of the modern busy scientific age by taking 'tranquillising' drugs.

Our efforts to develop new applications of science and technology are obviously aimed to increase our happiness. High productivity based on science can contribute much to our material welfare. But perhaps we ought at the same time to remember the good advice we used to get when we were children about high thinking and low living. In Mr Marin's words, 'it is beyond the imagination what freedom and happiness great science can produce for a civilisation of fine modest wants.' Perhaps the formula for serenity that he is advocating for the new commonwealth of Porto Rico may be of more general efficiency than any of the laboratory formulae for 'tranquillisers'.

The study of mankind, his behaviour, his troubles, his achievements and his weaknesses, is traditionally accepted as being at least a part of a humane and liberal education. This we can assert in spite of the pessimistic dictum that all we learn from history is that we learn nothing from history—that history, in the words of Gibbon, 'which is indeed, little more than the register of the crimes, follies and misfortunes of mankind'. The biological sciences have some way yet to go before their technical studies bring them fully into the field in which the motives of humanity are studied as well as the physiological reflexes. The geneticists who are beginning to identify the chemical composition of the genes that decide whether we shall be dark or fair, choleric or phlegmatic, intellectually inclined or addicted to golf, we have already discussed. The neurologists who are investigating the mechanism of the brain and the nervous system by which we perceive the existence of the outside world have equally far to go, but they also are advancing along the road by which science can develop from being an advanced exercise in mechanics or the solving of an intricate cross-word puzzle and become a worthwhile humane study.

Most of twentieth-century science, however, deals with things. And the danger of this kind of science and the scientists who work it is that it is treated as an activity of a morally neutral colour like cleaning one's teeth. It is customary for a motor-car manufacturer to describe his product as the most elegant and emotionally satisfying experience open to man on this planet, but in fact, as we all realise in our more adult moments, it is merely a device for moving about. The scientific philosophy *is* morally neutral when it is used to make *things*. By systematic experimentation, the study of metallurgy, a knowledge of the chemistry of combustion, the rheology of rubber and the mechanics of moving bodies, the motor-car manufacturer can produce cars that are capable of going faster and faster year by year. By applying scientific thinking to the manufacturing process as a whole, the men who run industry can make it more and more into a completely automatic process. The biologists and the 'pure' chemists and physicists can lay their claim to be pursuing a philosophical occupation; they are unlocking the secrets of Nature. The applied scientists, whom we so urgently seek to produce our economic wealth for us and who, with their automatic factories, their earth-moving equipment and their combine harvesters, provide us with mechanical 'slave' labour, have in their work no useful philosophy to live by. Their contribution is that they give us leisure; the freedom from the need to pay away our lives as hired labourers. The purpose to which we devote our 'spare' time—that is, the time when we are free people—is our own affair. It may be very different from the pursuit of truth as the scientist sees it.

The Devil is alleged to have described the Ten Commandments when he first heard of them as a remarkably mixed bag. Many of the prosperous twentieth-century citizens of today, whether consciously or unconsciously, conduct themselves to avoid if they can the seven deadly sins of the classical age: pride, wrath, envy, lust, gluttony, avarice and sloth. Perhaps it is simpler to make a working philosophy the other way round with good humour, kindliness and beauty set up as admirable objects for the pursuit of a civilised man. Science, the mode of behaviour that gives us our material comforts, has not, in the sense in which it is interpreted by its more orthodox exponents, much to say about any of these. On the other hand, if we can allow the scientist just a little room for manoeuvre, as I have tried to show in this book, there is perhaps something of each in his philosophy.

We can attribute good humour to the diligent purveyors of chlorophyll socks and the disciples of 'science' who believe in them. The Dalmatian coach-hound, the hippopotamus with allegedly deficient bile and the coloured dummy medicine, all to the frivolous mind have something of the amiably comic about them.

If we are intellectually honest we cannot claim for scientists as a group, that their prime and basic motive is to benefit their fellow men. And yet this *is* a motive of some force, and science has contributed many benefits. It is, therefore, not unfair to claim for it a measure of the virtue of kindliness.

So far as beauty is concerned, science as a philosophy has little to say. That is, when we mean beauty as apprehended by eye or ear. But for beauty as measured by the intellect, science can claim its major share. Truth is beautiful. When the mathematician describes the solution of a problem as 'elegant', it is to him as lovely as a lovely woman. The dispersal of error and the first glimpse of a new harmony in Nature have for the scientist a thrill equal to that of a piece of music or a sunset.

This book makes no claim to be a deep philosophical treatise. I have merely tried in it to show that science is something more than a process for inventing useful things—that it is, indeed, one way of finding out the truth. And besides trying to show something of what I believe science is I have, I hope, been able to demonstrate that some of the things that are attributed to it are often . . . nothing like science.